# The Great, Great Lakes Trivia Test

## The Who, What, Where, When, Why and How of Michigan

# Michael J. Thorp

SouThorp Publishers
Flint, Michigan

Published by
SouThorp Publishers
Flint, Michigan

Publisher's Cataloging-in-Publication Data
Thorp, Michael J.

   The great, Great Lakes trivia test : the who, what, where, when, why and how of Michigan / Michael J. Thorp. – Flint, Mich. : SouThorp-Publishers, 2010.p. ; cm.

   ISBN13: 978-0-9844975-0-8

   1. Michigan—History—Miscellanea. 2. Great Lakes (North America)—Miscellanea. I. Title.

F566.T56 2010
977.4—dc22                                      2010904242


Project coordination by Jenkins Group, Inc.
www.BookPublishing.com

FIRST EDITION

*Interior layout by Brooke Camfield*
*Cover design by Chris Rhoads*


Printed in the United States of America
14   13   12   11   10   •   5   4   3   2   1

# Dedication

For my Ginny, who thinks I can do anything.

For Grandma Ella (Curry) Thorp,
who believed me when I told her I would write a book.

For my daughters, Libby and Ella, who will be able to
tell my grandchildren that their grandpa wrote a book.

For my mom and dad, Barbara (DeGrow) Thorp and
LaVerne P. "Jim" Thorp, who made it possible.

And to my Champagne Club friends who love
Michigan, a good story, fun, and me.

# Contents

# Introduction

I have always been very interested in history and the story of Michigan and the Great Lakes. History is about people. It's really our story: how we live, who we are, how we got here. It's an amazing story. As any real historian will tell you, you cannot make up stranger stories than things that have really happened.

Over the years, I have collected facts of interest as I traveled around the region. The facts may have come from a pamphlet on a visitor center rack; perhaps they appeared on a placemat in a local restaurant or even had a small mention in a newspaper. I toss them all into my box that I save things in every year. The stories might be from some of the many wonderful local history books I have picked up and read, such as *Through the Years: Genesee*, by Alice Lethbridge; *A Look in Your Own Backyard: Tales of Caro and Nearby Places*, by Dorr Wiltse Sr.; *The History of Eagle Harbor Michigan*, by Clarence Monetto; *A Place Called Buick*, by Don Bent; and *Michigan: A History*, by Bruce Catton. I am an avid reader of *Michigan History* magazine and its many contributors; it tells some great stories.

Now I have written my own book, called *The Great, Great Lakes Trivia Test: The Who, What, Where, When, Why, and How of Michigan*. I took the many tidbits of Michigan and Great Lakes history and turned them into multiple-choice questions. Each question is a separate story about a person, a place, or an event, each one a little history on the topic.

As an old television and radio reporter with a deep interest in our story, I know that all inquiry, all stories, all facts can be brought to life by asking six important—even essential—questions. These are the same questions we all learned in elementary school, the questions that bring the story to light; these are the questions that are the chapters of my book.

Who? What? Where? When? Why? How?

# Introduction

*The Great, Great Lakes Trivia Test* is full of questions that will test your knowledge and pique your interest. Each question whets the appetite to find out more about the answer.

- Who was Leslie King Jr., and why is he famous?
- What was the smallest crowd to pay to see a Detroit Tigers baseball game?
- Where was the first known Christmas celebrated in Michigan?
- When did it become illegal to shoot cats in Michigan?
- Why do some believe that room 401 at Detroit's Grace Hospital is haunted?
- How far is the Mackinac Bridge designed to sway?

Each question and answer are separate stories about the people, places, things, and events in Great Lakes lore. Read a page or two or read the whole book in one sitting. I promise it will get you asking more questions and wanting to find out more.

- Who was the first to drive a horseless carriage in Michigan?
- What was the first law passed by a Michigan legislature?
- When was the first earthquake recorded in Michigan?

Take the test, see how much you know about our story, discover how far your curiosity can take you, and learn how we all fit in with our past and how it is connected to our future. Learn more about our story, the story of us: the people, places, and events of Michigan and the Great Lakes.

Michael J. Thorp
Author

*The Great, Great Lakes Trivia Test: The Who, What, Where, When, Why, and How of Michigan*

# "Who?"

## The great GREAT LAKES (*Who*) TRIVIA QUIZ

Who was the first major-league baseball player to win the most valuable player (MVP) award at two different positions?

    A.  Hank Greenburg
    B.  Babe Ruth
    C.  Frank Robinson

**ANSWER: A**
Hank Greenburg was one of the greatest players in the history of the game and was among the all-time greatest Tigers. He first won the MVP award in 1934 as a first baseman and repeated in 1940 as an outfielder.

One-time Flint inventor Lloyd G. Copeman was second only to Thomas Edison in number of patented inventions, with 650.

    Who is the famous female singer that is Lloyd Copeman's granddaughter?

    A.  Leslie Gore
    B.  Linda Ronstadt
    C.  Dusty Springfield

**ANSWER: B**
Flint inventor Lloyd Copeman's famous granddaughter is Grammy Award–winning singer Linda Ronstadt.

    Among Copeman's inventions are the rubber ice cube tray and the first no-run stocking. Copeman Boulevard in Flint, Michigan, is named in his honor.

Donald Riegle served in the Congress of the United States for more than 30 years as a representative of his hometown of Flint, beginning in 1976 as a U.S. senator.

    Who held the Senate seat before Don Riegle took office in 1976?

    A.  Lucious Lyon
    B.  Phil Hart
    C.  Robert Griffin

Who

**ANSWER: B**

Senator Phil Hart died on December 26, 1976, and was replaced by Don Riegle. The Hart Senate Office Building in Washington, D.C., is named in his honor.

Lucious Lyon was Michigan's first senator, and Robert Griffin was a Republican senator in the 1970s.

Many people change their names, for many reasons. Marion Morrison became John Wayne, and Bernie Schwartz became Tony Curtis.

Who was the famous Michigander first known as Leslie King?

A. Libby Maynard
B. Gerald R. Ford
C. Bob Seger

**ANSWER: B**

Leslie King became Gerald Ford when his mother married the man who became his stepfather and moved to Grand Rapids, Michigan. He was a U.S. representative from his hometown when he first was nominated to become vice president, after the resignation of Spiro Agnew. Then, upon the resignation of Richard Nixon on August 9, 1974, he became president of the United States (1974–1977).

Olivia P. "Libby" Maynard was the first woman to chair the Michigan Democratic Party (1979–1983). She ran for lieutenant governor of Michigan in 1990 and has been a regent at the University of Michigan since 1996. She is married to Olaf Karlstrom and lives in Goodrich.

Who was the founder of the Michigan cities St. Ignace and Sault Ste. Marie?

A. Father Gabriel Richard
B. Governor Lewis Cass
C. Father Jacques Marquette

**ANSWER: C**

Father Jacques Marquette founded both Upper Peninsula cities as mission sites. Marquette County, Michigan; the city of Marquette, Michigan; and Marquette University in Milwaukee, Wisconsin, were all also named in his honor.

4

Who from the classic television show *Laugh-In* was not born in Michigan?

A. Arte Johnson
B. Joan Worley
C. Dick Martin

**ANSWER: B**

Joan Worley is not from Michigan.

Arte Johnson was born in Benton Harbor in 1934, and Dick Martin was born in Detroit in 1922. Lily Tomlin, another star of *Rowan and Martin's Laugh-In*, is also a Michigan native.

Who was the first person to drive a "horseless carriage" in Michigan?

A. Henry Ford
B. Billy Durant
C. Charles King

**ANSWER: C**

On the night of March 6, 1896, Charles King, an inventor and engineer, drove his "horseless carriage" down Detroit's Antoine Street and turned down Jefferson and onto Woodward. It reached a speed of 8 miles per hour.

Legend has it that a curious young man named Henry Ford, who was riding a bike, was there and was inspired by the sight.

Former Tigers manager Sparky Anderson is now happily in retirement and has been inducted into baseball's hall of fame.

Who is Sparky Anderson, really?

A. Allan
B. William
C. George

**ANSWER: C**

Sparky Anderson's real first name is George.

Who did Bo Schembechler replace when he became head coach at the University of Michigan?

   A.  Bump Elliott
   B.  Stanley Blood
   C.  Fielding Yost
   D.  Benny Oosterbaan

**ANSWER: A**
Bo Schembechler replaced Bump Elliott as the head coach at the University of Michigan in 1969.
    Benny Oosterbaan and Fielding Yost were also former Michigan football coaches. Stan Blood is a friend of the author from Flint. He is a graduate of the University of Michigan and a vice president of the Genesee Regional Chamber of Commerce.

Who was the first radio voice of the Detroit Tigers?

   A.  Ernie Harwell
   B.  Ty Tyson
   C.  Harry Heilman

**ANSWER: B**
Ty Tyson broadcast the first Tigers game on the radio in 1927.
    Ernie Harwell broadcast baseball for more than 50 years, and Harry Heilman was also a Tigers radio announcer after his Hall of Fame career.

Who was the only hockey player in history to win an Olympic gold medal and a Stanley Cup championship in the same year?

   A.  Mike Eruzione
   B.  Ken Morrow
   C.  Chris Chelios

**ANSWER: B**
Ken Morrow was born in Flint and graduated from Davison High School. He won an Olympic gold medal and a Stanley Cup ring in 1980, the year of the "miracle on ice" when the U.S. hockey team beat the mighty Russians.

**Who**

Most of Michigan's governors were not natives of the state. Michigan's first governor, Stevens T. Mason, was born in Virginia. Many others were from New York and Massachusetts.

Who was Michigan's first native-born governor?

    A.   Governor Austin Blair

    B.   Governor Henry Crapo

    C.   Governor David Jerome

**ANSWER: C**
Governor David Jerome was born in Detroit in 1829. A businessman and state senator, he was elected governor in 1881, the first born in Michigan.

Who was the first Detroit Lions player to be inducted into the NFL Hall of Fame?

    A.   Dick "Night Train" Lane

    B.   Earl "Dutch" Clark

    C.   Alex Karas

**ANSWER: B**
The Detroit Lions' first inductee into the Pro Football Hall of Fame was Earl "Dutch" Clark.

Who was the Michigan auto dealer who served eight years as postmaster general in the Eisenhower administration?

    A.   William Garber

    B.   Arthur Summerfield

    C.   Otto P. Graff

**ANSWER: B**
Arthur Summerfield was a Flint Chevy dealer who was called to Washington, D.C., to serve in General Eisenhower's administration.

Among Michigan's first European visitors were many Catholic priests who came to save the souls of the native population.

Who was the Michigan priest known as the "snowshoe priest"?

**Who**

7

A.   Father Jacques Marquette
B.   Bishop Frederic Baraga
C.   Father Gabriel Richard

**ANSWER: B**
The snowshoe priest was Bishop Frederic Baraga. He was also called the parish priest of Lake Superior because his church included most of the western Upper Peninsula.

In Michigan, there are names for people of different occupations, hobbies, and habits.
Who were Michigan's "shanty boys?"

A.   Ice fishermen at Houghton Lake during Tip-up Town
B.   Detroit's first rap group
C.   Lumberjacks

**ANSWER: C**
"Shanty boys" were another name for the thousands of lumberjacks that were all over the state feeding lumber mills. They got the name because they lived in shanties in the woods.

Who was the first person born in Michigan to run for president on a major-party ticket?

A.   Lewis Cass
B.   Thomas Dewey
C.   Gerald R. Ford

**ANSWER: B**
Thomas Dewey of Owosso was the Republican nominee two times. He lost to FDR and also to Harry Truman. You probably remember the famous picture of the front page of the *Chicago Tribune* where the incorrect headline shouted, "Dewey defeats Truman."
Gerald Ford was born in Nebraska and grew up in Grand Rapids, and Lewis Cass was born in Massachusetts.

Who was president of the United States when Michigan finally became a state?

A. Millard Fillmore
B. Andrew Jackson
C. Andrew Johnson

**ANSWER: B**
President Andrew Jackson signed the papers that made Michigan a state in 1837.
    Millard Fillmore and Andrew Johnson both served as president.

Who was the first U.S. senator to represent Michigan in the nation's capital?

A. Lucious Lyon
B. Phil Hart
C. Arthur Vandenberg

**ANSWER: A**
While all three served as Michigan U.S. senators, the first was Lucious Lyon. He was appointed by the territorial legislature in 1835 and called on President Andrew Jackson in 1835.

Who was the famous abolitionist who in March of 1859 led 12 escaped slaves to Detroit on the Underground Railroad?

A. John Brown
B. Frederick Douglass
C. Sojourner Truth

**ANSWER: A**
Nine months before he was hung for leading an attack at Harper's Ferry, John Brown led 12 escaped slaves to Detroit, where he met with Frederick Douglass in a house on Congress Street.

Tigers great Hank Greenberg led the American League in home runs in 1946.
    Who was the next Detroit Tiger to lead the American League in home runs?

A. Willie Horton

Who

B.   Cecil Fielder

C.   Darrell Evans

**ANSWER: C**
Darrell Evans hit 40 dingers in 1985 to lead the American League. The first Tiger home run champ was Ty Cobb; he hit nine in 1909. Cecil Fielder hit 51 in 1990 to win the home run title and shared the title with Jose Conseco in 1991, with 44.

## Who was the founder of Chevrolet Motors in Flint?

A.   Billy Durant

B.   Louis Chevrolet

C.   A. B. C. Hardy

**ANSWER: A**
Though all three lived in Flint and were auto pioneers, it was Billy Durant, the founder of General Motors, who created Chevrolet Motors, using a French race car driver named Louis Chevrolet as the frontman.

## Before they were built, the Soo Locks in Michigan's Upper Peninsula were the source of a bitter fight in Washington, D.C., over funds to build them.

Who was the famous congressman that led the fight in Congress against building the Soo Locks in 1837?

A.   Henry Clay

B.   Andrew Johnson

C.   Abraham Lincoln

**ANSWER: A**
Congressman Henry Clay, who represented Kentucky in the U.S. House and Senate, led the fight against appropriations to build the Soo Locks at Sault Ste. Marie, Michigan. He said there were so few people living in the Upper Peninsula that it was "terra incognito."

Congress changed its mind and funded the project in 1853. The Soo Locks opened in 1855.

## Who is believed to be the first European to see the Great Lakes?

    A.  Father Jacques Marquette
    B.  Father Claude Allouez
    C.  Antoine de la Mothe Cadillac

**ANSWER: B**
Father Claude Allouez, a French Jesuit, saw Lake Superior on September 2, 1665.
    Father Allouez mapped all of Lake Superior and the northern parts of Lakes Huron and Michigan.
    Antoine de la Mothe Cadillac was the founder of Detroit.

---

Michigan is known all over the world as the home of the motor car. Who built Michigan's first self-propelled vehicle?

    A.  Judge Moses Wisner
    B.  Ransom Olds
    C.  Thomas and John Clegg

**ANSWER: C**
Thomas and John Clegg built what they called "the Thing" in Memphis, Michigan, in 1885. It was a steam-powered vehicle with seats for four.
    Ransom Olds founded Oldsmobile, and Judge Moses Wisner built his own horseless carriage in Flint.

---

Soon after the Wright brothers' first Kitty Hawk adventure, adventurers were flying in Michigan.
    Who was the first woman to ride in a plane in Michigan?

    A.  Mrs. Pamela Brown
    B.  Mrs. Russell Alger
    C.  Mrs. Neva DeGrow

**ANSWER: B**
In June of 1932, Mrs. Russell Alger went on an airplane ride with Frank Coffyn. They took off from Grosse Pointe Country Club.
    While Pam Angle Brown loves to fly and travel, she was far from the first woman to fly in an airplane. Pam is the mother of two and was born and raised in Flint, Michigan. She is a graduate of the University of Michigan. She is a former coworker of the author and spent 27 years in broadcast advertising. She now owns her own sales and marketing company, 3 Degrees Marketing.

Who

Neva (Rochester) DeGrow (1899–1972) was the author's maternal grandmother and was a teacher in a one-room school. She never rode in an airplane but did drive the earliest automobiles built in Flint.

In the language of Great Lakes seamen, who would be second in command to a ship's captain?

    A.  Able seaman

    B.  Mate

    C.  Seaman

**ANSWER: B**
The captain, or master, of a ship always counted on his mate to be his number 2. If there was more than one mate, the first mate was number 2, and the second mate was third in command.

Before Michigan became a state in 1837, it was a territory. Who was the U.S. president that signed the act creating the Michigan Territory?

    A.  George Washington

    B.  Thomas Jefferson

    C.  James Madison

**ANSWER: B**
The Michigan Territory was created when Thomas Jefferson signed an act that went into effect July 1, 1805. When Michigan's first territorial governor arrived in Detroit, he found that the city had been destroyed by fire.

Michigan is always remembered for its Motown music: the music of Smokey Robinson, Stevie Wonder, and the Temptations. But other famous musicians also call Michigan their home state.

Who of these famous music artists is NOT from Michigan?

    A.  Tommy James

    B.  Alice Cooper

    C.  Glenn Frey

**Who**

**ANSWER: NONE OF THE ABOVE**

It's a trick question: all three are from the Great Lakes State. Tommy James started the Shondells in Niles, Michigan, and had hits such as "Crimson and Clover" and "Mony Mony." Vincent Fournier is a Detroit-area preacher's son who became Alice Cooper, with hits including "Billion Dollar Babies" and "School's Out." Glenn Frey started in Royal Oak, Michigan, before he cofounded the Eagles with Don Henley and cowrote hits such as "Take It Easy," "Tequila Sunrise," and "Hotel California."

Who served as the Lapeer County prosecutor before becoming governor of Michigan?

    A.   Moses Wisner

    B.   Frank Murphy

    C.   John Swainson

**ANSWER: A**

Moses Wisner was governor from 1859 to 1860. A Pontiac attorney, he served as Lapeer County prosecutor. Wisner left office to form a regiment to fight in the Civil War. He died of typhoid while serving with his regiment in Kentucky in 1863, having never seen battle.

Who is the only member of the Baseball Hall of Fame who was born in Michigan and played for the Detroit Tigers?

    A.   Al Kaline

    B.   Charley Gehringer

    C.   Ty Cobb

**ANSWER: B**

While all three are members of the Baseball Hall of Fame and all spent most of their careers with the Tigers, only Charley Gehringer was born in Michigan, in Fowlerville.

Other Michigan-born members of the Baseball Hall of Fame include the Chicago Cubs' Kiki Cuyler, from Harrisville, Michigan; Tom Yawkey, owner of the Boston Red Sox, from Detroit; and Larry MacPhail, president of the New York Yankees, from Cass City.

Who was the first baseball player to hit a home run over the right-field roof at old Tiger Stadium?

**Who**

A. Babe Ruth
B. Ted Williams
C. Norm Cash

**ANSWER: B**
In May 1939, rookie slugger Ted Williams hit two homers at Tiger Stadium, leading the Boston Red Sox over the Tigers 7-6. The second homer was a monster blast over the right-field roof.

Roscommon County in Michigan's northern Lower Peninsula is known for beautiful lakes, great trout streams, canoeing, and golf.

Who is the auto pioneer credited with starting Roscommon County's first golf course?

A. Billy Durant
B. C. S. Mott
C. Henry Ford

**ANSWER: A**
Billy Durant, the founder of General Motors, built a big house on the Au Sable River in the 1920s. The home burned down many years ago, but its ruins are still visible to canoeists gliding down the river. He was also one of the founders of the Roscommon Golf Club.

Who was the first Michigan politician to mount a serious campaign for president?

A. Governor Lewis Cass
B. Governor George Romney
C. President Gerald R. Ford

**ANSWER: A**
In 1848, Governor Lewis Cass ran for president but was beaten by his Whig opponent, Zachary Taylor, who went on to become president of the United States.

Governor George Romney tried to get the Republican nomination in 1968, and Gerald Ford got the Republication nomination in 1976 but was beaten by Governor Jimmy Carter of the state of Georgia.

Who is Pamela Eldred, and what did she do in 1970?

    A.   She won an Olympic medal.

    B.   She won a record Michigan lottery jackpot.

    C.   She was named Miss America.

**ANSWER: C**

Miss Michigan Pamela Anne Eldred became Miss America in 1970.

---

Michigan is the home of only one U.S. president, Gerald R. Ford from Grand Rapids. He first served as vice president of the United States.

    Who was the first Michigan citizen to serve as vice president?

    A.   Lewis Cass

    B.   Thomas W. Ferry

    C.   Gerald R. Ford

**ANSWER: B**

U.S. Senator Thomas W. Ferry from Grand Haven, Michigan, was the first vice president from Michigan. Senator Ferry was elected as president pro tem of the Senate when President U. S. Grant's vice president, Henry Wilson, was scheduled to be out of town in March of 1875. At that time, that is how they decided who would preside over the Senate when the vice president was not available. When Vice President Wilson died, Senator Ferry served out his term until 1877.

---

Who is credited with creating the world's first carbonated beverage?

    A.   Joseph Coke

    B.   James Vernor

    C.   Josiah Hires

**ANSWER: B**

James Vernor invented Vernor's ginger ale. Before the Civil War began, Vernor, a Detroit pharmacist, concocted a new drink. When he was called off to war in 1862, he left the mixture in an oak cask in his pharmacy. He opened his keg when he returned from war in 1866 and found that the drink inside had been transformed by the aging process in the wood. What he found he called Vernor's.

Who

Who is the former governor of Michigan that became a Supreme Court justice?

    A.  Governor Josiah Begole

    B.  Governor Frank Murphy

    C.  Governor John Swainson

**ANSWER: B**

Governor Frank Murphy became Justice Murphy after he was appointed to the bench by President Franklin Roosevelt in 1940. He is remembered by labor as the governor who refused to end the Great Sit-Down Strike in Flint in 1937. Justice Murphy was born in Harbor Beach, Michigan, in 1890 and died in Detroit in 1949 at the age of 59.

Maybe you've heard of the "Georgia Peach," as baseball legend Ty Cobb was called. Perhaps you know that Michigan Governor G. Mennen Williams was nicknamed "Soapy" because of his family's men's toiletries business.

    Who was known as the "Hair Buyer"?

    A.  Henry Ford, for his wig business

    B.  Captain Henry Hamilton, Michigan's lieutenant governor in the 1770s

    C.  J. L. Hudson, founder of Hudson's Department Store

**ANSWER: B**

In the 1770s, Captain Henry Hamilton, the British commander at Fort Detroit and the territory's lieutenant governor, was known as "Hair Buyer Hamilton" for encouraging the native population to fight the American Revolution by paying for scalps.

In May of 1995, President Bill Clinton visited East Lansing to give the commencement address at Michigan State University. He was only the second president to speak at MSU.

    Who was the first sitting president to speak at Michigan State University's commencement?

    A.  Teddy Roosevelt

    B.  Harry S. Truman

    C.  Richard Nixon

**Who**

**ANSWER: A**
President Teddy Roosevelt visited the MSU campus in 1907 to speak at what was then the Michigan Agricultural College. The visit, on May 31, 1907, became Roosevelt Day in Michigan.

## Who was the first person to fly a plane?

A. Orville Wright
B. Augustus Moore Herring
C. Charles Lindberg

**ANSWER: B**
In October 1889, the *Benton Harbor News* reported that Augustus Moore Herring had flown his "contraption" for a brief time, five years before the Wright brothers. However, no photo was taken, so there is no "proof." In 1903, the Wright brothers did fly, and there is proof.

## Who famously said, "There is no such thing as a bad boy"?

A. Father Flannigan
B. Walt Disney
C. Floyd Starr

**ANSWER: C**
Floyd Starr, a graduate of Albion College, adopted 50 boys in 1913 and started the Starr Commonwealth for Boys on Montcalm Lake. Starr Commonwealth is still going strong, providing guidance to children.

## Each state gets to choose two people to represent the state with a statue in the Capitol in Washington, D.C.
### Who of these three has a statue in the Capitol?

A. Stevens T. Mason
B. Lewis Cass
C. Zachariah Chandler

**ANSWER: B, C**
Governor Lewis Cass and U.S. Senator Zachariah Chandler have statues in Washington, D.C.

Who

Stevens T. Mason was Michigan's first governor.

In Gordon Lightfoot's song "The Wreck of the *Edmund Fitzgerald*," he sings about the church that rang its bell "29 times for each man on the *Edmund Fitzgerald*." That church is the Mariner's Church in Detroit.

Who built the Detroit Mariner's Church?

A. The Catholic archdiocese
B. Detroit shipbuilders
C. A widow

**ANSWER: C**

The Detroit Mariner's Church was commissioned by Julia Ann Anderson, the widow of the commander of Fort Detroit, Colonel John Anderson. It was established in 1842 as a nondenominational church open to all, especially sailors.

Dorms have long been a part of college life.

Who built the first dorms on the campus at Michigan State University in East Lansing?

A. Joel Harrison
B. Gregory Brady
C. George Shaw

**ANSWER: A**

In the early 1850s, when MSU was still the Michigan Agricultural College, Joel Harrison built the first rooming house for students.

Greg Brady was a character on *The Brady Bunch* television show. George Bernard Shaw (1856–1950) was an Irish playwright who won a Nobel Prize and an Academy Award.

Who was the first woman licensed to fly an airplane in the United States?

A. Amelia Earhart
B. Lenore Croudy
C. Jeanette Rankin

**ANSWER: B**

Harriet Quimby was born near Manistee, Michigan, in 1885. She earned her pilot's wings in 1911 and was the second woman in the world to get a pilot's license, the first in the United States. She was the first woman to fly solo across the English Channel in 1912.

Lenore Croudy has been on plenty of planes but is not a pilot. She is a retired teacher and administrator in Flint, Michigan. She has served as trustee at Mott Community College since 1985 and as chair of the board of trustees since 1995. She served as chairperson of the Michigan Community College Association in 2008. She is a dear "lifetime" friend of the author.

The Mackinac Bridge officially opened at 2 p.m. on November 1, 1957.

Who was the first person to "officially" pay to drive across the "Big Mac"?

    A.   President Dwight Eisenhower

    B.   Al Carter

    C.   Jerry Preston

**ANSWER: B**

When the Mackinac Bridge opened in 1957, the first person in line was Chicago jazz musician Al Carter. He drove a 1951 station wagon.

Jerry Preston is a friend of the author who has been president of the Flint Area Convention and Visitors Bureau since 1996. He is active in the Michigan tourism industry, a longtime Boy Scout volunteer, and a licensed pilot.

Who of these famous musicians is an alumnus of Michigan State University?

    A.   Sonny Bono

    B.   Paul Stookey

    C.   Mitch Rider

**ANSWER: B**

While Mitch Rider and Sonny Bono were both born in the Great Lakes State, it was Paul Stookey, the Paul in Peter, Paul, and Mary, who attended MSU. He left college to found Peter, Paul, and Mary.

Who

Who of these Michigan governors was born in a foreign country?

A. Stevens T. Mason
B. William Woodbridge
C. George Romney

**ANSWER: C**
Governor George Romney was born in Chihuahua, Mexico. After serving as president of an auto company and as governor of Michigan, he was a member of the cabinet in the Nixon administration.

Who of these famous Hollywood stars was not born in Michigan?

A. Harry Morgan
B. Francis Ford Coppola
C. John Wayne

**ANSWER: C**
John Wayne was born Marion Michael Morrison in Winterset, Iowa.
Former *M\*A\*S\*H* and *Dragnet* star Harry Morgan was born in Detroit in April of 1915, and Academy Award–winning director Francis Ford Coppola is also a Detroit native, born there in April 1939.

Who is the governor of Michigan born in Alpena?

A. Governor Cyrus Luce
B. Governor William Comstock
C. Governor William Milliken

**ANSWER: B**
Governor William Comstock, Michigan's thirty-second governor, was born in Alpena in July of 1877.
Governor Luce was from Windsor, Ohio, and Governor Milliken is from Traverse City.

Who was the famous general and U.S. president that once lived in Detroit?

A. U. S. Grant
B. Dwight D. Eisenhower

C. Andrew Jackson

**ANSWER: A**
Civil War General and U.S. President U. S. Grant was stationed at Detroit during his service in the U.S. Army (1848–1849) and lived on West Fort Street near Livernois. The house is now located at the Michigan State Fairgrounds.

Whose name was on the Great Lakes freighter that sank on Lake Superior in the famous "Gales of November"?

A. Carl D. Bradley
B. Daniel J. Morrell
C. Edmund Fitzgerald

**ANSWER: A, B, C**
This is a trick question, as all three ships went down in a November storm on Lake Superior. The *Carl D. Bradley* went down in 1958, taking 33 lives, with two survivors. The *Daniel J. Morrell* went down in 1966, with 29 lost and one survivor. And, of course, the *Edmund Fitzgerald* went down in 1975, with all 29 crewmen lost.

Isolationists ruled the U.S. Senate before WWII. It was the change of heart by a leader of the isolationists in the Senate that helped get the United Nations approved.

Who is the senator that was instrumental in forming the U.N.?

A. Senator Harry Truman
B. Senator Strom Thurmond
C. Senator Arthur Vandenberg

**ANSWER: C**
Senator Arthur Vandenberg was a Republican from Grand Rapids, Michigan. World War II changed Senator Vandenberg's mind about getting involved with world events.

Who was the first African American to be awarded the Nobel Prize for Peace?

A. Ralph Bunche
B. Reverend Jesse Jackson

**Who**

C.  Elijah McCoy

**ANSWER: A**
Ralph Bunche was born in Detroit in 1904. He won the Nobel Prize in 1950 for negotiating a cease fire between warring countries in the Middle East.

Elijah McCoy was an engineer and inventor whose inventions inspired the saying "We want the real McCoy." He died in Detroit in 1928. Jesse Jackson is a well-known civil rights leader.

## Who of these TV stars was born in Michigan?

A.  Regis Philbin
B.  Ed McMahon
C.  William Shatner

**HEEEEEEEEEEEEEEERE'S THE ANSWER: B**
Ed McMahon (b. March 6, 1923; d. June 23, 2009) is a veteran TV personality who is best known as Johnny Carson's sidekick on *The Tonight Show*.

## Who was the first sitting president of the United States to visit Michigan?

A.  James Monroe
B.  U. S. Grant
C.  James Garfield

**ANSWER: A**
President James Monroe was the first president to visit Michigan while in office. He arrived in the frontier town of Detroit in August 1817. Residents of the city held a five-day celebration in honor of the visit.

## Michigan has produced a surprising number of astronauts for the NASA space program.

Who of these astronauts is not from Michigan?

A.  Colonel Jack Lousma
B.  Ed White
C.  Roger Chaffee

**ANSWER: B**

Lieutenant Colonel Ed White, from Texas, was the first American to walk in space. He died on January 27, 1967, in the fire that killed all three members of the *Apollo 1* crew.

Roger Chaffee, from Grand Rapids, Michigan, was a lieutenant commander in the U.S. Navy. He flew the U-2 spy plane during the Cuban Missile Crisis and died along with White and Colonel Virgil I. Grissom, a veteran of the *Mercury* and *Gemini* missions. Colonel Jack Lousma (USMC), also from Grand Rapids, Michigan, flew *Skylab* and piloted the space shuttle *Columbia* on a test mission.

*Sports Illustrated* magazine has been published since 1953.
Who was the first Michigan athlete to be featured on the cover?

    A.  Al Kaline

    B.  Ted Lindsay

    C.  Ron Kramer

    D.  Chris Hamilton

**ANSWER: A**

Al Kaline was the first Michigan-based athlete on the cover of *Sports Illustrated* magazine in May 1956.

Red Wing legend Ted Lindsay was on the November 1957 cover, and UM football star Ron Kramer made the cover in November 1956.

Chris Hamilton was never on the cover of *Sports Illustrated*, but he read it a lot. He is a friend of the author and a fellow Eagle Scout. He is retired from Delphi and is currently executive director of the Old Newsboys of Flint, a group that raises funds so "every child can have a Christmas." A graduate of Linden, Michigan, High School, he played on Purdue University's only team of Rose Bowl champions in 1967. He also has made more than 4,000 people turtles. (YBYSAIA)

Everyone likes ice cream sodas!
Who invented ice cream sodas?

    A.  Fred Sanders

    B.  Bill Knapp

    C.  David Crabill

**ANSWER: A**

Fred Sanders, a Detroit candy maker, invented the ice cream soda. The story goes that one night, around 1875, some customers ordered sweet cream sodas. Sanders didn't have sweet cream, so he used ice cream instead.

**Who**

Dave Crabill, of Swartz Creek, enjoys a good ice cream soda, but he didn't invent them. Dave is a husband, a father, and a friend of the author. He is an entrepreneur, writer, and small-business marketing wiz, thanks to Don and Mary Lou Crabill. Find him at http://www.escmi.com.

The city of Detroit was founded in 1701 by a French explorer. Who was the French explorer who founded the Motor City?

A.  Father Gabriel Richard
B.  Antoine de la Mothe Cadillac
C.  Francois Detroit

**ANSWER: B**

Detroit was founded by Antoine de la Mothe Cadillac, who arrived at the mouth of the Detroit River in July of 1701 and immediately began construction of Fort Ponchartrain to protect French Michigan from the English.

Father Gabriel Richard (1767–1832) was a French Roman Catholic priest who became a delegate from the Michigan Territory to the U.S. House of Representatives in 1823. He was the cofounder of the University of Michigan. Father Richard died of cholera in Detroit and was buried in a crypt in St. Anne's.

Royalty came to Michigan in June of 1982. Who was it?

A.  Prince Philip, England
B.  Queen Beatrix, Netherlands
C.  King Juan Carlos, Spain
C.  Duke Olaf Karlstrom, Sweden

**ANSWER: B**

Her Royal Highness Queen Beatrix Wilhelmina Armgard of the Netherlands came to Michigan in 1982. Not surprisingly, she stopped in Holland and Grand Rapids.

While Olaf Karlstrom is a prince of a man, he is not a duke. He is a practicing attorney and friend of the author. He is a former Flint city attorney, past chairperson of the board of Hurley Medical Center, and a graduate of the University of Michigan Law School. He is married to Libby Maynard and lives in Goodrich.

Who is the only baseball player in major-league history to hit grand slams in consecutive at bats?

24

A. Babe Ruth
B. Jim Northrup
C. Barry Bonds

**ANSWER: B**
In the Detroit Tigers' golden year, 1968, Tiger outfielder Jim Northrup came to the plate with the bases loaded two times in a row and blasted home runs, leading the Tigers to a 14-3 win at Cleveland.

The largest American flag ever made now hangs at the Smithsonian Institution in Washington, D.C.
Who made it?

A. The Smithsonian
B. A department store
C. The U.S. Navy

**ANSWER: B**
The world's largest flag was made by Hudson's Department Store in Detroit in 1949. It was 235 feet by 104 feet, and it took more than a mile of rope to fly it. It was flown for the last time on Flag Day in 1976 as part of the U.S. Bicentennial celebration. Hudson's donated the flag to the Smithsonian after the July 4 celebration.

Who was the first future president to visit Michigan?

A. William Henry Harrison
B. Abraham Lincoln
C. Franklin D. Roosevelt

**ANSWER: A**
On May 10, 1803, William Henry Harrison, who was at the time governor of the Indiana Territory, arrived in Detroit for a visit. He came to Michigan three more times before he was elected president of the United States in 1841.

Lots of famous people are from Michigan.
Who of these was not born in the Wolverine State?

A. Charles Lindberg
B. Aretha Franklin

Who

25

C.  Henry Ford

**ANSWER: B**
The queen of soul, Aretha Franklin, was born in Washington, D.C.
Aviator Charles Lindberg is from Detroit, and auto pioneer Henry Ford is a native of Dearborn, Michigan.

Many streets and buildings in Flint were named for former GM executives, including GM presidents.
Who of the following was not a GM president?

A.  Harlow Curtice
B.  Alfred Sloan
C.  Arthur Sarvis

**ANSWER: C**
Arthur Sarvis, for whom the Sarvis Center in Flint's Cultural Center was named, was a banker and the first executive director of the college and cultural center in Flint.
Alfred Sloan, the namesake of Flint's Sloan Museum, was president of General Motors in the 1920s, and Harlow Curtice, who had a building on the Mott Community College campus named for him, was GM president from 1953 to 1958.

Who was the first Michigan astronaut to get into outer space?

A.  Brewster Shaw
B.  Jack Lousma
C.  James McDivitt

**ANSWER: C**
James McDivitt became the ninth man in space in 1965 and the first Michigander. During the same flight, Edward White became the first to walk in space.
Brewster Shaw, a retired Air Force colonel, is from Cass City, Michigan. He graduated from Cass City High School in 1963. Jack Lousma, a marine colonel, was born in Grand Rapids, Michigan.

Who was the former University of Michigan baseball coach who created the major-league farm system?

26

A. Branch Rickey
B. Connie Mack
C. Leo Durocher

**ANSWER: A**
That Michigan baseball coach was Branch Rickey. He is also known as the man who broke baseball's color barrier by signing Jackie Robinson to a major-league contract. He received his law degree from the University of Michigan while working as a baseball coach from 1910 to 1913. His record as coach was 69-31-4.

Tiger Stadium, in Detroit, was first called Navin Field. It opened on April 20, 1912.
Who was the first player to score a run at Navin Field?

A. Shoeless Joe Jackson
B. Ty Cobb
C. Honus Wagner

**ANSWER: A**
Shoeless Joe Jackson, then of the Cleveland Indians, scored that first run at Navin Field, although the Tigers won the game 6-5 in 11 innings.

Who was the first person to drive across the Mackinac Bridge?

A. Mike James
B. Governor G. Mennen Williams
C. Nancy Williams

**ANSWER: C**
On November 1, 1957, at the grand opening ceremonies, Governor Williams was asked to be the first to drive across the bridge. However, it was discovered that he didn't have a driver's license, so his wife, Nancy, had to drive.
   While Mike James has driven across "Big Mac" many times, he was not the first. He is a friend of the author and is president of the Genesys Ambulatory Division and other organizations within Genesys Regional Medical Center. Before joining the health system, James was a health care attorney. He is married to Leslie, a teacher, and lives in Flint.

Who of these literary giants did NOT write in Michigan?

Who

A. Ernest Hemingway
B. Carl Sandburg
C. Henry Wadsworth Longfellow

**ANSWER: C**
Henry Wadsworth Longfellow never wrote in Michigan, though he did write "The Song of Hiawatha," which is based on a Michigan Native American legend.
Ernest Hemingway spent summers near Petoskey, Michigan, and Carl Sandburg spent many summers writing at his cottage on Lake Michigan near New Buffalo, Michigan.

Who of the following television and movie stars were born in Michigan?

A. Della Reese
B. Martin Milner
C. Ron Howard

**ANSWER: A, B**
Della Reese, the star of television's *Touched by an Angel*, was born in Detroit in 1932. Martin Milner, the star of *Route 66* and *Adam 12* was born in Detroit in 1931.
Actor/director Ron Howard is from Hollywood.

Who was the first Detroit Tigers player to be paid $100,000 a year?

A. Hank Greenburg
B. Al Kaline
C. Denny McLain

**ANSWER: B**
In 1971, Tigers great Al Kaline signed the richest contract, at that time, in Tigers history. The story goes that Kaline had turned down $100,000 the year before because he thought it was too much to pay a baseball player. What would Kaline be worth today?

Who was the first coach of the Michigan State football team?

A. Duffy Dougherty
B. Henry Keep
C. Charles Bachman

**ANSWER: B**
The year was 1897, and Henry Keep became the coach at the school then known as the Michigan Agricultural College and the team called the Aggies.
Charles Bachman was a Spartan coach in the 1930s and Duffy Dougherty a coach in the 1960s.

Who was the first woman to serve as lieutenant governor of the state of Michigan?

A. Libby Maynard
B. Martha Griffiths
C. Matilda Dodge-Wilson

**ANSWER: C**
The first woman to serve as Michigan's lieutenant governor was Matilda Dodge-Wilson. She was appointed on November 19, 1940, by Governor Luren Dickinson (he became governor when Governor Frank Fitzgerald died in office). Dodge-Wilson served for 45 days.
Martha Griffiths served as a U.S. congresswoman from 1955 to 1974 and later as Michigan lieutenant governor under Governor James Blanchard for two terms.

Who was the first Catholic priest to serve in the Congress of the United States?

A. Father Gabriel Richard
B. Father Andrew Greeley
C. Father Jacques Marquette

**ANSWER: A**
Father Gabriel Richard, of Detroit, took his seat in Congress in 1823 while Michigan was still a territory.

An official holiday in Michigan is October 21, known as Will Carleton Day.
Who was Will Carleton?

A. An explorer
B. A soybean scientist
C. A poet

**ANSWER: C**
Will Carleton was a poet, born on October 21, 1840. *Harper's Weekly* once said he was more popular and widely read than Longfellow or Whittier. His most famous poem is "Over the Hill to the Poor House," which, by Michigan law, must be read in class by teachers on his birthday.

Who was the governor of Michigan known as "Potato Patch"?

    A.  Hazen Pingree

    B.  Josiah Begole

    C.  G. Mennen Williams

**ANSWER: A**
Governor Hazen Pingree was a shoe manufacturer from Detroit. He was a mayor of Detroit and a Michigan governor from 1897 to 1901. He picked up the name "Potato Patch" during the depression of 1893, when he advised the jobless to grow their own food.

Who of these Michigan governors served the longest time in office?

    A.  William Milliken

    B.  James Blanchard

    C.  G. Mennen Williams

**ANSWER: A**
Governor William Milliken served in office for 13 years, from 1969 to 1982.
    G. Mennen "Soapy" Williams served 11 years in office, starting in 1949. James Blanchard served two terms in office, from 1983 to 1991. Terms limits limiting a governor to two terms in office took effect during Governor John Engler's term, 1992–2002. He was allowed to serve a third term, making him the third-longest-serving governor in Michigan history.

The Renaissance Center in Detroit is the city's most identifying landmark since its completion in 1977. Today, it is the world headquarters of the General Motors Corporation.

    Who was the guiding force behind the construction of the Renaissance Center?

    A.  Mayor Coleman Young

    B.  Henry Ford II

C.  Governor William Milliken

**ANSWER: B**
Henry Ford II began to push suppliers and others to fund the building after the Detroit riots of 1967. It is ironic that the grandson of Henry Ford would be the force behind the creation of what is now GM's world headquarters.

Who was the first Detroit Tigers baseball player to be named to the Baseball Hall of Fame?

A.  Charlie Gehringer
B.  Ty Cobb
C.  Hank Greenburg

**ANSWER: B**
Cobb was actually the first player elected to the Baseball Hall of Fame in 1936, along with Babe Ruth, Honus Wagner, Christy Mathewson, and Walter Johnson.
Both Charlie "the Mechanical Man" Gehringer and "Hammering" Hank Greenburg are also members of the Hall of Fame who played for the Detroit Tigers.

Michigan was one of the first states in the nation with automobiles, so it follows that it would have the first driver's licenses. Michigan was also the first state to have a specialty driver's license, a chauffer's license, for professional drivers.
Who was the first to get a chauffer's license?

A.  Henry Ford
B.  Governor G. Mennen Williams
C.  David Buick

**ANSWER: A**
Henry Ford took the first test and became the first licensed chauffer in the country.

Publishers are the people who print newspapers and sell them. Without them and reporters, there would be no freedom of the press.

Who was the first publisher to distribute a newspaper on a train?

A.  William Randolph Hearst
B.  Joseph Pulitzer
C.  Thomas Edison

**ANSWER: C**

Thomas Edison, the inventor, became the first publisher to sell a paper on a train. It was called *The Weekly Herald* and was published in February 1862 on a run between Port Huron and Detroit.

Who was the French fur trader who built Fort St. Joseph on the present site of Port Huron, Michigan?

A.  Daniel Duluth
B.  Etienne Brulé
C.  Pierre Charlevoix

**ANSWER: A**

The trader who built Fort St. Joseph at Port Huron was Daniel Duluth, who would later found Duluth, Minnesota.

Etienne Brulé was another French trader who would discover Isle Royale, and Pierre Charlevoix was a French missionary.

For many politicians, just getting the party nomination for president is the pinnacle of success.

Who was the presidential candidate that received his party's nomination not once but twice and lost both times?

A.  Lewis Cass
B.  Thomas E. Dewey
C.  Robert Taft

**ANSWER: B**

Thomas E. Dewey was the Republican candidate for president in 1944, when he lost to Franklin D. Roosevelt, and in 1948, when he was defeated by Harry S Truman. He was born in 1902 in Owosso, Michigan; was a graduate of the University of Michigan; and was a governor of New York for more than 10 years.

Built in 1817 on Mackinac Island, the Stuart House is one of the oldest homes on the Island and in Michigan.

Who is the Stuart House on Mackinac Island named for?

    A.  Robert Stuart, explorer and businessman

    B.  Stu Stuart, son of Bonnie Prince Charlie Stuart of Scotland

    C.  James Stuart, actor

**ANSWER: A**

Robert Stuart (1785–1843) was an explorer from Scotland. He came to Canada in 1807 to work in the fur trade. He was a partner of John Jacob Astor in the American Fur Company. The house was built as his home and as the headquarters of the American Fur Company. He also helped blaze the Oregon Trail, the gateway west of the Rockies, in 1812. He served as treasurer of the state of Michigan from 1840 to 1841.

Stu Stuart is not of royal but of comedic blood. He has been a stand-up comic and sitcom writer since 1991. He has the funniest show on Mackinac Island, where he has performed for many summers. He lives in northern California and Mackinac Island, Michigan. He is a beer enthusiast who loves his Belgian ales. Check out his Belgian Beer Me Web site, http://www.belgianbeerme.com.

Who was a famous disc jockey born in Michigan?

    A.  Casey Kasem

    B.  Dick Clark

    C.  Johnny Burke

**ANSWER: A**

Casey Kasem, who made American Top 40 a radio classic, was born Kemel Amen Kasem in Detroit in 1932.

Dick Clark created *American Bandstand* on television, and Johnny Burke is the morning host on WHNN radio in Saginaw, Michigan.

Most big companies, such as auto companies, are owned by stockholders that have little connection to their past. The Ford Motor Company is different in that respect because the Ford family owns a large percentage of the stock in the company. The most recent member of the Ford family to lead the company is William Ford,

Who

33

the son of William Clay Ford and great-grandson of the founder. Four members of the Ford family have led the auto company.

Who in the Ford family has NOT been the head of Ford?

A. Henry Ford
B. William Clay Ford
C. Edsel Ford

**ANSWER: B**

William Clay Ford has never been at the helm of Ford Motor Company. He does own a lot of stock and is the owner of the Detroit Lions.

---

The Flint Bluegrass Festival began in 1978 as part of a larger celebration, Flint Festivals. Subtitled "Country in the City," it honored the heritage of area residents drawn north by the lure of a big paycheck from the auto plants. The festival, a volunteer project, ran for 10 years (1978–1987) and featured nationally known stars such as John Hartford, Doc Watson, the Carter Family, and Bill Monroe, as well as local musicians such as Mustard's Retreat, Neil Woodward, the Cloverleafs, the McLain Family, and Old South.

Who was the youngest person to appear on the stage of the Flint Bluegrass Festival?

A. David Carter Jones (age 15), with the Carter Family in 1983
B. Nancy McLain (age 14), with the McLain Family in 1979
C. Brian "Possum" Kennedy (age 9), with the Lonesome River Boys in 1985
D. Katie Whiteside (age 4 months), with the Whitesides in 1984

**ANSWER: D**

The youngest was Katie Whiteside. She was 4 months old when she was taken on stage by the Whitesides in 1984. She now lives in Tennessee and manages a small business. Her mom, Mary Ann Chick Whiteside, was a lead volunteer for the festival, starting in 1979. Her dad, Lawrence Whiteside, joined in 1983. The author and his wife, Ginny, along with hundreds of others, were among the volunteers.

Who

# "What?"

## The great GREAT LAKES (*What*) TRIVIA QUIZ

Albert Champion was brought to Flint by GM founder William C. "Billy" Durant. In Flint, Champion founded AC Spark Plug and later Champion Spark Plug.

What did Albert Champion do in his native France before he came to America and Flint?

    A.  He was a race car driver.

    B.  He was a world bicycle champion.

    C.  He was a wine maker.

**ANSWER: B**

Albert Champion was a world bicycle champion. He raced in France before starting the Champion Ignition Company in Boston. He came to Flint in 1908 at Billy Durant's invitation and changed the name to AC Spark Plug.

In October 1901, a Bay City school teacher named Annie Edson Taylor performed an amazing feat.

What wild feat did Taylor accomplish?

    A.  She swam the Straits of Mackinac.

    B.  She survived a ride over Niagara Falls.

    C.  She scaled the state capitol dome.

**ANSWER: B**

Annie Edson Taylor was the first person known to survive a ride over Niagara Falls. Others had tried but didn't make it. Taylor designed the wooden barrel herself and had it made at a Bay City cooperage.

Detroit Tigers pitcher Dennis McLain was the last 30-game winner in the major leagues. He was suspended by the Tigers and later by Major League Baseball in 1970.

What did Denny McLain do in 1970 to get suspended?

    A.  He got involved with gamblers.

    B.  He doused a sportswriter.

    C.  He carried a gun.

**What**

**ANSWER: A, B, C**

McLain, baseball's last 30-game winner, was suspended three times in 1970. The first time, he was suspended for being involved with bookmakers. He was suspended a second time when he doused a sportswriter with water. His final suspension in 1970 was for carrying a concealed weapon.

What was Detroit native James McGinnis famous for?

    A.  Joining a circus

    B.  Playing baseball

    C.  Being mayor of Detroit

**ANSWER: A**

James McGinnis ran away from home to join the circus when he was 14. He changed his name to James Bailey and became partners with a guy named Phineas Barnum. Together they created the greatest show on earth, the Barnum & Bailey Circus.

Melville Ruben Bissell, from Grand Rapids, Michigan, was a famous inventor. In fact, you most likely use a descendant of one of his inventions often.

    What did Melville Bissell invent?

    A.  Bicarbonate of soda

    B.  Carpet sweeper

    C.  Dish soap

**ANSWER: B**

Bissell invented the carpet sweeper in 1876. His name is still attached to a company that makes vacuums.

Prisons, often called correctional facilities, are placed all over the country, from the largest walled prison in the country in Jackson, Michigan, to some that look like community colleges.

    What was the Dunes Correctional Facility at Saugatuck, Michigan, before it became a prison?

    A.  A seminary

    B.  A supermarket

C. It's always been a prison.

**ANSWER: A**
Before the Dunes Correctional Facility became a prison, it was the St. Augustine Seminary. It was purchased by Michigan in 1978 for $4 million.

---

In our country, we pay attention to firsts: the first female governor, the first African American president, the first man to attend an all-woman college.

What was unique about Michigan Governor Frank Fitzgerald's two terms in office?

A. They were nonconsecutive.
B. He was appointed to both terms.
C. He resigned both times.

**ANSWER: A**
Governor Fitzgerald's terms were nonconsecutive. He was Michigan's thirty-fourth and thirty-sixth governor. First elected in 1934, he lost reelection to Frank Murphy but came back to beat him in 1938. He died in Grand Ledge at the age of 54, only two and a half months after retaking office. He is also the only Michigan governor to die in office.

---

Michigan natives have played a great role in space exploration. They have been a part of the *Mercury, Gemini, Apollo,* and space shuttle programs.

What Michigan city boasts two natives that have been to the moon?

A. Detroit
B. Jackson
C. Ann Arbor

**ANSWER: B**
The city of Jackson is the hometown of both General James McDivitt, *Gemini 4, Apollo 9,* and Colonel Alfred Worden, *Apollo 15.* Both have also been to the moon.

Captain Jerry M. Linenger, M.D., M.S.S.M., M.P.H., Ph.D., retired NASA astronaut and US Navy flight surgeon, was raised in Eastpointe, Michigan. Linenger logged approximately fifty million miles in more than two thousand Earth orbits during his nearly five month mission aboard the Russian space station Mir. At the completion of his mission, he had spent more continuous time in space than any American man.

In 1939, an automobile company offered air conditioning as one of the accessories on a new car.

What car company was the first to offer air conditioning in its vehicles?

    A.  Packard

    B.  Buick

    C.  Studebaker

**ANSWER: A**

It was the Packard Motor Company that first offered the opportunity for a cool ride in 1939. Soon others followed suit.

The Great Lakes are all connected by rivers or straits.

What connects Lake Huron and Lake Superior?

    A.  Straits of Mackinac

    B.  Detroit River

    C.  St. Mary's River

**ANSWER: C**

Lakes Huron and Superior are connected by the St. Mary's River, which includes the Soo Locks.

    The Detroit River, which is also technically a strait, connects Lakes Erie and Huron, and the Straits of Mackinac connect Lakes Michigan and Huron.

Birch Run, Michigan, in Saginaw County was named after the creek that runs through it. But the community also went by an earlier name.

What was the earlier name for Birch Run, Michigan?

    A.  Deer Lick

    B.  Busted Hoof

    C.  Painful Toe

**ANSWER: A**
Birch Run was known as Deer Lick in 1863, when the government named the local post office Deer Lick, Michigan. The name was changed to Birch Run in 1868.

Railroads were an important part of early American life. Most every important town had a depot. Otisville, Michigan, near Flint, had a stop on the Pere Marquette Railroad, but locals called it something else.

What did the locals call the train that came through town every day?

    A.  Father Marquette Express
    B.  Huckleberry Railroad
    C.  Flint Line

**ANSWER: B**
The Huckleberry Railroad went from Flint to Otisville, into the Thumb of Michigan and beyond. It got the name because riders could get off in the front car, pick berries, and get back on the last car. Today, part of the line is working at Genesee County Park's historic Crossroads Village.

Career choices for women have expanded greatly over the past century. Back in 1914, a government report listed the top three occupations for working women.

What job was a working American woman most likely to have in 1914?

    A.  Teacher
    B.  Servant
    C.  Stenographer

**ANSWER: B**
In 1914, the government counted 33,000 women who were servants, 17,000 who were teachers, and 7,000 who were stenographers.

**What**

Many have given their businesses their own names: Wal-Mart, for Sam Walton, and McDonalds, for the brothers who created the fast-food restaurant.

What one of these businesses is the name of one man?

    A.  Sears "Bucky" Roebuck

    B.  Montgomery "Monte" Ward

    C.  Waldorf "Wally" Astoria

**ANSWER: B**

While Sears and Roebuck were partners and the Waldorf-Astoria Hotel in New York was the combination of two hotels, Montgomery Ward is the name of a man and his business. Ward was a salesman at a general store in St. Joseph, Michigan, before he went on to create his mail-order method of selling.

What do country star Roy Clark, the late Ethiopian Emperor Haile Selasie, and former West German Chancellor Willy Brandt have in common?

    A.  They were all born in Ireland.

    B.  They all played musical instruments made in Michigan.

    C.  They all appeared at a University of Michigan lecture series.

**ANSWER: B**

They all played guitars made by the famous Gibson Guitar Company of Kalamazoo. Gene Autry, Bill Monroe, and Mick Jagger were all known to play a Gibson as well. Founded in Kalamazoo in 1896, the Gibson Guitar Company moved to Nashville, Tennessee, in 1984.

Fire departments have been around almost as long as there have been fires. The Lansing, Michigan, Fire Department made world history in 1909.

What happened to the Lansing Fire Department in 1909?

    A.  It fought a skyscraper fire.

    B.  It crashed its fire truck.

    C.  It hired a full-time fireman.

**ANSWER: B**
The Lansing Fire Department's first motorized fire truck crashed into a hitching post on wet pavement. This incident is thought to be the first ever crash of a motorized fire truck.

The Great Lakes are a great place for sailing, boating, fishing, and all kinds of recreation. But they are also a freeway of goods from around the world. Many kinds of ships ply the waters, and lake sailors have names for them.

What do Great Lakes sailors call seagoing vessels?

A. Big boys
B. Tankers
C. Salties

**ANSWER: C**
Lake sailors call seagoing vessels "salties" and those that ply the lakes exclusively "lakers." A laker has a bump on the bow, or front of the ship, while a saltie's bow is straight.

There's nothing as sure as death and taxes. Michigan's first tax was put into effect in 1805 by the territorial government when most residents were traders and trappers. The tax was called a "capitation" tax.

What was a capitation tax?

A. A tax on the head of every animal trapped
B. The cost to visit the state capitol
C. A tax on each person

**ANSWER: C**
A capitation tax was a tax on the head of each person over 16 who lived in the state. The tax was $1 and was paid by 525 citizens.

Michigan is blessed with outstanding institutions of higher learning. Michigan Technological University was built in Houghton, about as far north as you can go in Michigan's Upper Peninsula, in 1886.

What was Michigan Tech first known as?

**What**

A.  Michigan College of Mining and Technology
B.  Houghton University
C.  Michigan Mining School

**ANSWER: C**
When founded in 1886, Michigan Technological University was called the Michigan Mining School. It had no buildings, so classes were held at the Houghton Town Hall.

The Detroit Tigers baseball team has suffered through many very bad seasons. Usually when a bad team is on the field, attendance is bad.
    What was smallest crowd ever to see a Tigers baseball game?

A.  404
B.  1,404
C.  2,404

**ANSWER: A**
In September 1928, the Tigers faced the Boston Red Sox in front of a crowd—if you could call it that—of just 404 spectators. Not surprisingly, they lost 8-0.

Battle Creek, Michigan, is known as the Cereal City because it is the birthplace of both Kellogg and Post. Post cereal, founded by Charles W. Post in 1895, had a hit with its first product, Grape Nuts. Next came Post Toasties, which became quite controversial under its original name.
    What was Post Toasties cereal first called?

A.  Corn Post
B.  Elijah's Manna
C.  Post Crunchies

**ANSWER: B**
Post Toasties, Post's first attempt at corn flakes, were first called Elijah's Manna, with a box that featured the prophet Elijah. Church groups were outraged over the use of Elijah as a cereal mascot. Post said, "Perhaps no one should eat angel food cake, live in St. Paul, or work for Bethlehem Steel." However, Mr. Post

changed his tune when the biblical backlash began to cut into his sales. In 1908, he renamed the cereal as Post Toasties.

Michigan is known for its lakes, rivers, and streams; it is, after all, the Great Lakes State. Some rivers are deep enough for freighters, others perfect for canoes.

What river in Michigan is the longest?

    A.   Grand River
    B.   Manistee
    C.   Pere Marquette

**ANSWER: A**
The longest river in Michigan is the Grand River; it runs about 300 miles from Lake Michigan.

The second-longest river is the Manistee, at about 200 miles. The shortest river in Michigan is the Saginaw River, which is large enough for freighters but only about 20 miles in length.

Once people are settled in an area, one of the first things you can expect is a newspaper. One of Michigan's oldest newspapers is the *Detroit Free Press*, founded in 1831.

What was the *Detroit Free Press* called when it was first published?

    A.   Democratic Free Press and Michigan Intelligencer
    B.   The Free Press News
    C.   Free Press and Western News

**ANSWER: A**
Published even before Michigan became a state, the *Detroit Free Press* was first called the *Democratic Free Press and Michigan Intelligencer*.

Michigan soldiers have seen action in our nation's wars since the Revolution. Well over 1.6 million have served their country from the state of Michigan.

What war was deadliest for Michigan's veterans?

**What**

A. Civil War
B. WWII
C. Vietnam

**ANSWER: A**
Not surprisingly, more Michigan soldiers lost their lives in the Civil War than in any other conflict. In the Civil War, 14,350 Michiganians lost their lives; however, only about 4,200 actually were killed in battle, with the rest dying from disease and illness.
More than 10,000 men and women from Michigan lost their lives in Vietnam.

A foundry is a place where metal is cast into useful products. The East Jordan Iron Works, in East Jordan, Michigan, is one of the oldest and largest foundries in Michigan.
What is made at the East Jordan Foundry?

A. Chassis for automobiles
B. Manhole covers
C. Big machines

**ANSWER: B**
Now called East Jordan Iron Works, the company is a leading manufacturer of construction castings, fire hydrants, tree grates, and much more, including manhole covers. The company is located in East Jordan, Michigan, where the foundry has been operating since the late 1800s.

Throughout Michigan and the Midwest, there was a well-known concern called the "Butterfield Circuit."
What was the Butterfield Circuit?

A. A florist company
B. A dairy
C. A chain of theaters

**ANSWER: C**
The Butterfield was a chain of movie theaters operated all over Michigan, founded in about 1921 by Colonel W. S. Butterfield, from Holland, Michigan. The circuit was dismantled in the early 1980s.

Going "up north" is what people in Michigan, Ohio, Illinois, and Indiana do. They go "up north" to play in some of Michigan's beautiful lakes, and there are a lot of them. One of the most beautiful was first known as Forginson Lake.

What Michigan Lake was first known as Forginson Lake?

A. Houghton Lake
B. Higgins Lake
C. Torch Lake

**ANSWER: B**

In 1839, John Brink of the State Geological Survey mapped the lake and named it Forginson Lake. In 1852, it was named for Sylvester Higgins, a topographer friend of William Burt, Michigan's first official surveyor. The Chippewas called it Majinabeesh, "sparkling water." It is not known whether Higgins ever saw the lake that bears his name.

Michigan's Upper Peninsula is mostly covered in forests and lakes. Over the years, its natural resources, such as fur, copper, iron, and lumber, have been key to its economy.

What is the major industry in Michigan's Upper Peninsula today?

A. Copper and iron mines
B. Lumber
C. Tourism

**ANSWER: C**

Though fur, mining, and lumber have been major industries in the past and they still contribute to the economy, today the U.P.'s top economic engine is tourism.

Cities, towns, and villages in Michigan come in all shapes and sizes. The differences have more to do with rules for governing than with size.

What village is the largest in Michigan?

A. Caro
B. Escanaba
C. Royal Oak

**What**

**ANSWER: A**
The largest village in the state of Michigan is Caro, at the center of Michigan's Thumb region.
Escanaba and Royal Oak are officially cities.

---

People often have what they think are good excuses for speeding. Cops will tell you they have heard them all, and they keep track.

What is the most common excuse that people give to police when they are pulled over?

    A.  They have to use the bathroom.
    B.  The wind pushed them.
    C.  They are late for work.

**ANSWER: A**
The most common excuse for speeding, according to police, is "I have to use the bathroom." Some cops collect excuses. A couple of favorites: "I was speeding to keep up with the cars behind me" and "My wife is going to get pregnant tonight, and I want to be there when it happens."

---

Over the years, many service organizations have changed their bylaws to allow women to become members. The Elks, Lions, Rotary, and Jaycees are among many. In 1984, the Supreme Court of the United States ruled that all male civic groups had to allow women to join.

What did the Jaycees in Zilwaukee, Michigan, do?

    A.  Had a big party
    B.  Disbanded
    C.  Elected a woman president

**ANSWER: B**
The 23 members of the Zilwaukee Jaycees burned all their Jaycee shirts and jackets and their charter in a 1984 bonfire and disbanded. A new chapter, with more politically correct members, was formed soon after, with 12 men and 12 women.

---

The year was 1934, and Mr. G. A. Richards bought a professional football team in Ohio and moved it to Detroit. That team is now the Detroit Lions.

What was the Detroit Lions' original name?

A. Spartans
B. Buckeyes
C. Wheels

**ANSWER: A**
Mr. Richards bought the Portsmouth Spartans. They became the Lions when they got to Detroit.

In the Great Lakes states, we celebrate the all-American Independence Day every July 4. The Founding Fathers imagined it would be a day of parades, family gatherings, and political speeches.

What is the one thing the Founding Fathers could not have imagined about how we celebrate Independence Day?

A. Fireworks
B. People getting the day off from work
C. It's on July 4.

**ANSWER: C**
Our Founding Fathers declared Independence from England on July 2, 1776. However, the Declaration of Independence was published on July 4, and that became the day we celebrate our nation's birth.

The early 1900s were a time of great population growth in Michigan. During the years from 1910 to 1920, one Michigan community grew faster than any other.

What Michigan community led the nation in growth between 1910 and 1920?

A. Flint
B. Hamtramck
C. Highland Park

**ANSWER: B**
According the U.S. Census Bureau, between 1910 and 1920 Hamtramck grew from 3,589 to 45,615 residents, becoming the country's fastest-growing community.

**What**

The U.S. Navy names ships after people (*USS John F. Kennedy*), places (*USS Missouri*), and things (*USS Typhoon*). Mostly, though, ships are named for people and places.

What native of Genesee County, Michigan, has a U.S. Navy ship named for him?

    A.  Senator Donald Riegle

    B.  Admiral Thomas Hart

    C.  Lieutenant Governor William Fenton

**ANSWER: B**

The navy named the destroyer escort the *USS Thomas Hart* for Davison native Thomas Hart. Admiral Hart was born in Davison in 1877 and joined the navy, becoming one of the youngest graduates of the U.S. Naval Academy. After he retired from the service, he became a U.S. senator from Connecticut.

The Michigan legislature has passed many laws since the Michigan Territory was founded in 1805, but there was a first.

What law was the first ever to pass a Michigan legislature?

    A.  A pay raise for lawmakers

    B.  A tax on the fur trade

    C.  The establishment of a territorial seal

**ANSWER: C**

In July 1805, Governor William Hull signed Michigan's first law, an act that described and adopted an official territorial seal. Earlier in the year, President Thomas Jefferson appointed Hull Governor, as well as Indian agent, of the recently created Michigan Territory.

Pastors often get into more than just church issues in their sermons. In 1906, Father Timothy Murphy at St. Joseph Catholic Church in St. Joseph, Michigan, issued an ultimatum that began a statewide crusade.

What was Father Murphy's ultimatum?

    A.  Women should wear hats in church.

    B.  Men should remove hats in church.

    C.  Women wearing pants is a sin.

**What**

**ANSWER: A**

Father Murphy was upset that women had begun to come to Mass without wearing hats. Pastors of all faiths liked Father Murphy's idea, and they began a campaign to get women to wear their hats to church.

In 1921, inmates at the maximum-security Marquette prison in Michigan's Upper Peninsula were given a special task. What was the task?

    A.  Become gourmet chefs

    B.  Work as clothing models

    C.  Design an escape-proof cell

**ANSWER: C**

Prisoners who had tried elaborate and daring escapes were put to work designing an escape-proof cell. In exchange for a reduction in their sentences, they designed the $80,000 cell, and their fellow inmates built it.

The Detroit and Pontiac Railroad was one of the first railroads in the country when it began operation in 1838.

    What powered the Detroit and Pontiac Railroad when it began operation?

    A.  Steam power

    B.  Man power

    C.  Horsepower

**ANSWER: C**

Steam locomotives were hard to come by in the Michigan wilderness, but horses were plentiful.

There are lots of nicknames in sports. "Magic" Johnson, "Sparky" Anderson, and "Woody" Hayes are examples. One of the University of Michigan's greatest football coaches had a great nickname, Bo Schembechler.

    What was Coach "Bo" Schembechler's real first name?

    A.  George

    B.  Glenn

**What**

C.  Garland

**ANSWER: B**

Bo Schembechler's real first name was Glenn (Glenn Edward Schembechler). His nickname "Bo" came from his sister's attempts to say "brother" when they were young. Schembechler died at age 77 on the day before the Michigan–Ohio State game in 2006.

Going to court is never fun, unless you happen to be an attorney. There are local municipal judges and state judges.

What do we call judicial districts, overseen by state judges, in Michigan?

A.  Benches
B.  Districts
C.  Circuits

**ANSWER: C**

Judges that work for the state are called circuit judges because they used to ride a "circuit" to bring the law to courtrooms throughout their districts.

What did the U.S. Marine Corps do in 1978 that made history?

A.  Land on the wrong beach
B.  Promote a woman to the rank of general
C.  Change the Marine Corps hymn

**ANSWER: B**

In May 1978, the marines named Margaret Ann Brewer, of Durand, Michigan, brigadier general.

There are many famous names in Michigan: the Ford family, the Motts, the Dows.

What were the names Brixcoe, Hacket, Jackson, and Handley known for?

A.  A law firm
B.  Car companies
C.  Michigan counties

**ANSWER: B**
Brixcoe, Hacket, Jackson, and Handley were all car companies that produced vehicles in Jackson, Michigan.

---

Michigan's first state capital was in Detroit. In 1847, the Michigan legislature moved the capital to Lansing, to be more centrally located.

What was in Lansing when the capital was moved there in 1847?

   A.  A small town with a railroad depot
   B.  An Indian village with a ferry across the Red Cedar River
   C.  A log cabin and sawmill

**ANSWER: C**
When the Michigan state capital was moved to Lansing, it was literally dropped into the middle of the wilderness. In 1847, Lansing consisted of a log cabin and a sawmill.

---

Michigan State University is the world's first land grant agricultural college. It was first known as Michigan Agricultural College and later Michigan State University.

What was the area where MSU was located first called?

   A.  East Lansing
   B.  Collegeville
   C.  Sparta

**ANSWER: B**
The area where MSU was created was known as Collegeville until 1907, when the name was changed to East Lansing.

---

Politicians love to choose state flowers, birds, insects, fish, and even stones.

What is the official state fossil of Michigan?

   A.  Petoskey stove
   B.  Mastodon
   C.  There is no such thing for the state of Michigan.

**What**

In 2002, the mastodon was declared by the Michigan legislature to be the state fossil. Fossils of mastodons have been found at more than 250 locations around the state.

You've probably heard of Tin Pan Alley in New York. From the 1890s through 1955, Tin Pan Alley dominated the music scene in America. One city in Michigan had many contributors to that era's music.

What Michigan city had the biggest influence on the music of Tin Pan Alley?

    A. Detroit
    B. Saginaw
    C. Lansing

**ANSWER: B**
Saginaw had a number of songwriters who worked on New York's Tin Pan Alley, including Dan Russo, who wrote "Toot Toot Tootsie Goodbye"; Gerald Marks, who wrote "All of Me"; and Isham Jones, who wrote "It Had to Be You." Those are just a few of the great songs written by great songwriters from Saginaw.

There are four major interstate freeways in Michigan: I-75, I-69, I-94, and I-96. What interstate freeway ends (or begins, depending on how you view it) in Michigan?

    A. I-75
    B. I-69
    C. I-94
    D. I-96

**ANSWER: A, B, C, D**
All of the interstate freeways that come to Michigan terminate there: I-75, from Ft. Myers, Florida, to Sault Ste. Marie, Michigan; I-69, from Indianapolis, Indiana, to Port Huron, Michigan; I-94, from Billings, Montana, to Port Huron, Michigan; and I-96, from Muskegon, Michigan, to Detroit's Ambassador Bridge.

Michigan is known for its lighthouses. As a matter of fact, Michigan has more lighthouses than any other state.

What lighthouse in Michigan is the oldest?

    A.  Fort Gratiot Light

    B.  Round Island Light

    C.  Eagle Harbor Light

**ANSWER: A**

Michigan's oldest lighthouse is the Fort Gratiot Light at Port Huron, just north of the Blue Water Bridge, built in 1861. The original tower was established in 1820.

There seems to be a license for everything. You need a license to drive a car; to fly a plane; to teach school; and to be a doctor, a pharmacist, and a builder.

    What of the following occupations needs a license?

    A.  Butter grader

    B.  Minnow dealer

    C.  Garbage feeder

**ANSWER: A, B, C**

Believe it or not, in the state of Michigan you need a license to sell minnows, to grade butter, and to be a garbage feeder. By the way, a garbage feeder feeds garbage to swine.

Towns large and small all over the country identify themselves with products, events, and people. In Traverse City, it is cherries; in Detroit, it is motors, as in Motor City.

    What is Mesick, Michigan, in Wexford County known as the capital of?

    A.  Mushrooms

    B.  Gladiolas

    C.  Hamburgers

**ANSWER: A**

Mesick is the mushroom capital of Michigan. It is believed that it is the only place in the world where all five varieties of morel mushrooms are found. Until the 1950s, Mesick was the gladiola capital, but a virus killed most of those flowers.

**What**

Flint, Michigan, has had at least seven different minor-league baseball teams.

What was the nickname of the first Flint minor-league team that took the field?

A. Flint Vehics
B. Flint Buicks
C. Flint White Stockings

**ANSWER: C**
The Flint White Stockings took the field in 1902, but they were not very good. Halfway through the year, they changed their name to the Flint Colts. That didn't help, either. There were several teams called the Flint Vehics over the years, none very successful.

The last minor-league team in Flint, the Flint Arrows, played at the city's Atwood Stadium in 1951.

Summer celebrations are big business in cities all over the Great Lakes states. The Potato Festival, the Bean Festival, and the Sugar Festival are examples.

What of these festivals are actual festivals celebrated in Michigan?

A. Fish Sandwich Festival
B. Bologna Festival
C. Mastodon Festival

**ANSWER: A, B**
The Fish Sandwich Festival is celebrated in Bayport, Michigan, in August, and the Bologna Festival is the big summer party in Yale, Michigan, held in late July.

Michigan does not have a mastodon festival—yet.

The first road maps in Michigan were issued in 1912. They showed only roads that received state funding. By 1924, maps looked more like what we see today.

What appeared on a Michigan map in 1978 that caused an uproar?

A. An advertisement for Strohs
B. The words "goblue" and "beatosu"
C. A dirty limerick

**ANSWER: B**
In 1978, State Highway Commissioner Peter Fletcher, a good Wolverine fan, secretly inserted "Go Blue" and "Beat OSU" in the northern Ohio part of the map. A limited number of the maps were issued before the joke was discovered and fixed. By the way, Michigan beat OSU that year 14-3.

Most historians consider the June 5, 1944, D-day invasion of Europe by the Allies to be the beginning of the end for the Germans. Citizens all over the country contributed to the final victory with victory gardens, rationing, bond drives, and metal collection. One Michigan high school had a special connection with the D-day invasion.

What was the connection of Greenville High School to the D-day invasion?

A. Several former students were there.
B. It bought a glider.
C. It designed a landing craft.

**ANSWER: B**
The students of Greenville High School sold $72,000 in war bonds to have the Gibson Refrigerator Company in Greenville build the first glider to land at Normandy on D-day.

Former GM division Delphi is struggling to survive. The company, an automotive parts supplier, has had several names.
What was Delphi's original name?

A. AC Spark Plug
B. Champion Spark Plug Company
C. Action Parts

**ANSWER: B**
Delphi was first known as the Champion Spark Plug Company and was based in Flint, Michigan. It was founded by Albert Champion, one of a long list of automotive pioneers who lived and worked in Flint.

It takes someone of a certain age to remember the days when we would actually "spin a record." Michigan has played an important role in the record industry.

What famous record label carried the slogan "It's what's in the groove that counts"?

A. Tamla
B. Gordy
C. Motown

**ANSWER: B**
The record label with the groovin' slogan was Barry Gordy's Gordy Records. Of course, all of those labels were founded and owned by former Detroit autoworker Barry Gordy.

Education has always been important in Michigan. The state even founded its first college, the University of Michigan, in 1817.

What is Michigan's second college?

A. Kalamazoo College
B. Michigan State University
C. Eastern Michigan University

**ANSWER: A**
Michigan's second-oldest college is Kalamazoo College, founded in 1833. It was followed by Albion College in 1834 and Eastern Michigan University in 1844.

Baseball has been broadcast on radio since radio stations first began to broadcast. In some ways, baseball is perfect for description over the air.

What radio station first carried the Detroit Tigers?

A. WCAR
B. WJR
C. WWJ

**ANSWER: C**
The first radio broadcast of a Detroit Tigers baseball game was on Michigan's oldest radio Station, WWJ, in 1927. The station first went on the air on August

20, 1920, with the call sign 8MK. It is believed to be the first station to broadcast news reports regularly, as well as the first regularly scheduled religious broadcast and play-by-play sports broadcast. The announcer Ty Tyson called that game from what was at that time called Navin Field.

After the assassination of Dr. Martin Luther King Jr. and the passage of the King federal holiday, many communities named streets after him.

What was the first street in Flint, Michigan, named for an African American?

    A.   Martin Luther King Avenue

    B.   Floyd McCree Drive

    C.   Herman Curtis Boulevard

**ANSWER: C**

Herman Curtis was a safety engineer at GM's Fisher Body plant and was honored by having Hillcrest Boulevard located in Flint, Michigan renamed Herman E. Curtis Boulevard in 1975.

Former Flint Mayor Floyd McCree was the first African American elected mayor of a large city in America. Floyd McCree Drive is named after him.

A refreshing question about soda pop: The most famous soda pop is from the Coke Company; it was founded in Atlanta, Georgia, in 1886. It was intended as a patent medicine when it was invented in the late nineteenth century by John Pemberton.

What soda pop company was founded in Michigan?

    A.   Faygo

    B.   Squirt

    C.   Vernor's

**ANSWER: A, B, C**

All three of these soft drinks were first made in Michigan. Faygo was made by two Russian immigrant brothers named Feigenson in Detroit in 1907. Squirt was founded in Holland, Michigan, in 1938. Vernor's was first made by pharmacist James Vernor in Detroit in 1866. It is the oldest pop brand in the country.

Faith has always been an important part of American life. Going to church on Sunday morning is as American as apple pie.
What American city has the most churches per capita?

    A.  Detroit, Michigan

    B.  Hamtramck, Michigan

    C.  Grand Rapids, Michigan

**ANSWER: C**
Grand Rapids, Michigan, has more churches per capita than any other American city. It also has the most religious radio and television stations per capita.

People make up names for places, things, and people that sometimes fit and that sometimes make you wonder where they came from.
What is a tridge?

    A.  A trailer with a refrigerator

    B.  A three-way bridge

    C.  A troll that protects a bridge

**ANSWER: B**
It is famous in Midland, Michigan, as the tridge. It is a three-way bridge that was built in 1981 at the confluence of the Chippewa and Tittabawassee rivers, at a place called Chippewassee Park. It is the only one known to exist in the world.

Here is some geography trivia for those in the Great Lakes states.
What state does not share a land border with Michigan?

    A.  Illinois

    B.  Indiana

    C.  Wisconsin

**ANSWER: A**
The state of Illinois does not share a land border with Michigan. Indiana, Wisconsin, and Ohio do share a land border with it.

Here is a good fish tale: What is the largest fish species in lakes throughout the Great Lakes states?

A. Salmon
B. Sturgeon
C. Northern pike

**ANSWER: B**

While northern pike and salmon can grow to be quite large indeed, the boney-plated sturgeon can grow to more than 200 pounds and live for more than 100 years.

It's capital time again. What are the Oceana County, Michigan, communities of Shelby and Hart known as the world capital of?

A. Asparagus
B. Peas
C. Pigeons

**ANSWER: A**

Hart and Shelby are known as the asparagus capital of the word, but the area has also been known as the pea capital and once was considered the greatest pigeon roost in the United States.

The third-oldest city in Michigan is Monroe.
What was it first called?

A. Poletown
B. Frenchtown
C. Germantown

**ANSWER: B**

Monroe was first called Frenchtown. It got that moniker in 1784 when 100 French families from Canada settled on the River Raisin. In 1817, Frenchtown was renamed in honor of newly elected President James Monroe after he visited the frontier town.

In 1920, federal agents got into the act of regulating fishing in the Detroit River. They outlawed a certain kind of fishing.
What did federal agents forbid fisherman to catch in 1920?

**What**

A. Whitefish
B. Whiskey
C. Shipwrecks

**ANSWER: B**
During Prohibition, revenuers discovered that rumrunners had been driving truckloads of Canadian whiskey across the frozen Detroit River in the winter and often would go through the ice. The folks of Detroit soon discovered the whiskey graveyard and took up fishing as a sport.

When automobiles were first on the road, officials discovered that they had to make up rules of the road. Otherwise, it would be mass confusion on the few roads that existed.

What traffic-flow feature was introduced in Michigan in 1911?

A. Painted white centerline
B. Mile markers
C. Stop sign

**ANSWER: A**
In 1911, road officials added a white painted centerline to the roads to help drivers figure out what side of the road they should drive on.

Another capital question: In central Michigan lays Montcalm County and the tiny village of Trufant. Trufant is known for its Labor Day Festival.

What is Trufant the capital of?

A. Frogs
B. Stumps
C. Junk cars

**ANSWER: B**
Trufant is the stump capital of the United States. In the mid-1800s, the original white pine forest was clear-cut, leaving only stumps. When Danish farmers took over the land, they cleared the stumps and found that they made very nice fences.

It does get cold in Michigan. But when we think cold, we're usually talking 10–15 degrees below 0. Now that is cold, but it has been colder—much colder—in Michigan.

What is the coldest temperature ever recorded in Michigan?

A. –22
B. –43
C. –51

**ANSWER: C**
Believe it or not, on February 9, 1934, the temperature in Vanderbilt, Michigan, got down to 51 below 0. Vanderbilt is in northern Lower Michigan.

A great venue in Flint, Michigan, is its Atwood Stadium, an 11,000-seat stadium located along the Flint River that opened on June 8, 1929. It has hosted high school football; rock concerts, such as Herman's Hermits and the Who; presidential visits from FDR and JFK; minor-league baseball; football; and many more events.

What was on the site of Flint's Atwood Stadium before the stadium?

A. A farm
B. A dump
C. A carriage factory

**ANSWER: B**
It was a community dump site for many years before it became a community project to clean it up to create the site to build the stadium. There was an island in the river at that site that was filled in to create more room for the stadium.

Michigan is the Great Lakes State, well known for its lakes large and small. But in a quirk of geography, there is one county in the state—only one—that does not have a natural lake.

What county in Michigan does not have a natural lake?

A. Midland County
B. Saginaw County
C. Oceana County

**What**

The only lakeless county in Michigan is Saginaw County. It does have more than 160 miles of rivers and streams—but no lake. The rivers are the Cass, Flint, Saginaw, and Tittabawassee.

Frankenmuth, Michigan, is famous for its chicken dinners and German hospitality. It is one of the top tourist attractions in the Midwest. It is not the only Michigan community that is famous for its chicken cuisine.

What other place in Michigan is famous for chicken dinners?

    A.  Standish
    B.  Pinconning
    C.  Sterling

**ANSWER: C**
Sterling is the home of Iva's Chicken Dinners. It all started in 1938 when Iva started renting out rooms in her large farmhouse to local oil rig workers. She fed them chicken dinners, and Iva's is still serving those tasty chicken dinners in Sterling.

Michigan has been part of the British Empire and New France, as well as the United States.

What Michigan city has been under the flags of four countries?

    A.  Niles
    B.  Sault Ste. Marie
    C.  Detroit

**ANSWER: A**
The city of Niles has had the flags of the United States, England, France, and, for one day, Spain. Spanish explorers came to Michigan from the Mississippi River and got as far as Niles before they turned back.

Roads to and through any community are very important to the commerce and livelihoods of the people who live there. Flint, Michigan, is the "Vehicle City," and because its citizens built carriages, cars, and trucks, the roads were very important.

What was the first road to go through the city of Flint?

A. Saginaw Road
B. Detroit Street
C. Grand Traverse

**ANSWER: C**

The first real road through and to Flint was Grand Traverse. It started as an Indian trail that ran from Detroit to Saginaw. It was called the Grand Traverse because it was the easiest place to cross the Flint River. It was also the place where the first European settler built a trading post. Today it remains a major route through town.

So you think gangs are a problem today? They have always been a problem. The most violent and corrupt gang in Michigan's history was not one that started in the 1990s; it has its roots much earlier.

What is the most infamous gang ever in the history of Michigan?

A. Bennet Gang
B. Purple Gang
C. James Gang

**ANSWER: B**

That infamous and deadly gang was the Purple Gang in Detroit. In the 1920s and 1930s, it ran the Detroit crime scene. The gang started its deadly spree by bringing liquor across the Detroit River from Canada during Prohibition and eliminating all the competition.

One of the most beautiful places in the Great Lakes is Mackinac Island. The island does not allow motor vehicles, sits in the middle of the Straits of Mackinac, and is graced by century-old Victorian homes, a lighthouse, and two forts. That's right: besides Fort Mackinac, there is another fort on Mackinac Island.

What is the name of the *other* fort on Mackinac Island?

A. Fort George
B. Fort Holmes
C. Fort Michilimackinac

**ANSWER: B**

The other fort on Mackinac Island is Fort Holmes. It was built in 1812 by the British during the War of 1812; they named it Fort George. In 1815, the Americans got the island back from the British and took possession of Fort Mackinac and Fort George. They renamed it Fort Holmes, in honor of Major Andrew Holmes, who was killed in the 1814 Battle of Mackinac Island.

Flint, Michigan, is known as the birthplace of the United Auto Workers Union, in the Sit-Down Strike in 1936–1937. It has a strong tradition as a union town.

What group of workers is believed to be the first unionized workforce in Flint?

    A.  Auto workers

    B.  Coal miners

    C.  Cigar makers

**ANSWER: C**

Believe it or not, Flint was a major manufacturer of cigars in the late 1800s. The Cigar Makers Union Local 186 was founded in Flint in 1881.

Service clubs are important parts of local communities. The Rotary, Kiwanis, Lions, Elks, Jaycees, Junior Leagues, and so many more have made major contributions. A service club that was founded in Detroit was called the Supreme Lodge of the Benevolent Order of Brothers.

What did that group change its name to?

    A.  Elks

    B.  Kiwanis

    C.  Rotary

**ANSWER: B**

First chartered in Detroit in 1914, the Benevolent Order of Brothers became the Kiwanis in 1915. Kiwanis is an international organization that comprises around 8,000 clubs in 96 countries with more than 260,000 members. The name Kiwanis means "we trade" or "we share our talents" and was based on a Native American expression, *Nunc Kee-wanis*. "We build" was also the original motto of Kiwanis. The current motto is "Serving the children of the world."

There are many interesting islands in and around the Great Lakes. Whether the islands are in a big lake or on one of the hundreds of small lakes, they have great history and amazing stories and legends. The strangest island in the region—maybe in the world—is the small pine tree–dotted island in Lake Dubonnet near Interlochen, Michigan.

What is so strange about this island?

A. It moves.
B. It glows.
C. It's the home of Bigfoot.

**ANSWER: A**

The island in Lake Dubonnet moves. According to local legend, it's the world's only floating island. Fishermen and DNR officials have witnessed the slow movement of the one-acre island with 40-foot pine trees when the wind is high.

The city of Detroit is home to the world-famous Detroit Institute of Arts and many other art museums and galleries.

What is considered the largest work of art in Detroit and even the state of Michigan?

A. The Fisher Building
B. Diego Rivera murals
C. The Ambassador Bridge

**ANSWER: A**

The largest work of art in Detroit and Michigan is considered to be the Fisher Building. It was built by the seven Fisher brothers, who made their fortunes in the auto industry. Albert Kahn, the great architect, designed the building, which was to have been the first of three buildings in one complex. That dream ended with the Depression. The building holds many grand artistic touches, including at least 40 varieties of marble.

The Diego Rivera murals are big but not as big as the Fisher Building. The murals, called *Detroit Industry*, are considered the finest example of the Mexican muralist's work in the United States; Rivera considered the murals the most successful work of his career. In 1932, Rivera was commissioned by Edsel Ford, president of the Arts Commission, as well as of Ford Motor Company, and Dr. William Valentiner, director of the Detroit Institute of Arts, to create two murals for the museum in its Garden Court.

What

It was quite controversial to add fluoride to city water supplies. Dentists said it would cut tooth decay and cavities, and, in hindsight, they were right.

What Michigan city was the first in the country to take the highly controversial move to add fluoride to its water supply?

A.  Grand Rapids
B.  Alpena
C.  Midland

**ANSWER: A**
The first city in the country to add fluoride to its water was Grand Rapids, Michigan. It began adding the fluoride in January 1945. Adding fluoride to water supplies is now considered one of the great successes of public health, and most cities around the country add fluoride to water supplies.

Pickles come in many varieties: dill, sweet, and kosher, for example. Pickles are mentioned by Shakespeare and are used as a Christmas decoration, an old German tradition. Parents hide a pickle in the Christmas tree, and the child who finds it gets an extra present. One Michigan community celebrates this tradition by calling itself the Christmas pickle capital of the world.

What city is the Christmas pickle capital?

A.  Frankentrost
B.  Ishpeming
C.  Berrien Springs

**ANSWER: C**
The Christmas pickle capital is Berrien Springs, Michigan. It has a Christmas Pickle Festival that includes a Dillmeister, to lead the parade, a Pickle Princess, and lots of pickle ornaments.

Michigan is known for its outstanding educational opportunities for all. A Michigan college was among the first in the country to confer degrees on women.

What Michigan college was the first to confer degrees on women?

68

A. Hillsdale College
B. Alma College
C. Eastern Michigan University

**ANSWER: A**

Hillsdale College, then called Michigan Central College, was only the second college in the nation to confer degrees on women when it was founded by Baptists in Spring Arbor, Michigan, in 1844. In 1853, the college moved and changed its name to Hillsdale College.

---

Great literature can be set anywhere, and Michigan has been the setting for many classic books and stories.

What piece of literature had a Michigan setting?

A. *Anatomy of a Murder*
B. "The Song of Hiawatha"
C. *The Doll Maker*

**ANSWER: A, B, C**

*Anatomy of a Murder* was set in Big Bay, Michigan, in the Upper Peninsula. It was written by Michigan Supreme Court Justice John D. Voelker under the pen name Robert Traver. It was based on a 1952 murder case in which he was the defense attorney. It was made into an Otto Preminger film with stars James Stewart and George C. Scott. Henry Wadsworth Longfellow's "The Song of Hiawatha" was a poem based on Michigan Native American legends. *The Doll Maker* is a novel by Harriette Arnow about a woman who leaves the peace of Kentucky to go to wartime Detroit.

**What**

---

Today, we can have ice anytime. They even play ice hockey in the heat of the Deep South. Colleges have played hockey for decades, in the early days outdoors and at the whim of nature.

What Big 10 school was the first to have an indoor ice rink?

A. Michigan State University
B. University of Wisconsin
C. University of Michigan

**ANSWER: C**
The University of Michigan was the first in the Big 10 to have refrigeration equipment. They started freezing the ice in December of 1928.

Michigan has many rivers and streams. They are important for freight transport, sport fishing, and boating.

What major river is the shortest in Michigan?

    A.  Au Sable River
    B.  Saginaw River
    C.  Detroit River

**ANSWER: B**
The Saginaw River, while an important transportation route, is only 20 miles long.
    The Detroit River is the widest, at 2,200 feet. The Au Sable River is 129 miles long; it is also the fastest and one of the greatest fishing and canoeing rivers in the world.

While the political parties today have been around for a century, there was a time when parties other than Democrats and Republicans were dominant. At least one party was formed in Michigan.

What political party was formed in Jackson, Michigan, in 1854?

    A.  Mugwumps
    B.  Republican Party
    C.  Free Soil Party

**ANSWER: B**
According to legend, the Republican Party was formed "under the oaks" in Jackson, Michigan, on July 6, 1854. Michigan was a strong antislavery state, and the party was formed to fight slavery. Four years later, Abraham Lincoln was the party nominee for president. The rest is history.

The Great Lakes are a hotbed for hockey—not surprising for a place that gets very cold in the winter. In 1923, an NHL team began to play in Detroit.

What was the name of the first NHL team in Detroit?

A. Red Wings
B. Cougars
C. Motors

**ANSWER: B**

Detroit's first NHL team was called the Cougars. They played at the Border Cities Arena in Windsor, Ontario, Canada, because Olympia was under construction. They lost the first game to the Boston Bruins, 2-0. In 1927, they moved to Olympia, in Hockeytown, and became the Detroit Red Wings.

Halloween is supposed to be scary and eerie. Some stories add to the legend of Halloween.

What happened on Halloween in 1926 in Detroit that makes some believe it is a supernatural place?

A. Chief Pontiac's ghost visited.
B. The Detroit River turned red.
C. Harry Houdini died.

**ANSWER: C**

The great magician Harry Houdini died in Detroit on Halloween night in 1926 in room 401 of Grace Hospital. He had been injured in Montreal on October 23 when a man hit him in his stomach before he was ready and ruptured his appendix. Houdini traveled to Detroit, performed his show, and collapsed on Halloween. Just before he died, he said he would contact his wife from the other world, if it was possible. So far, no word from Harry Houdini.

Michigan is the Great Lakes State, which means the state has a lot of water.

What Michigan county has the most water?

A. Cheboygan County
B. Bay County
C. Roscommon County

**What**

**ANSWER: A**
Michigan's Cheboygan County, with Mullet, Black, and Burt lakes, has the most water in the state, with more than 46,000 acres. Rounding out the top four wettest counties are Chippewa, Mackinac, and Roscommon counties.

Barry Gordy, at Michigan's own Motown Records, discovered many very talented people and groups. One of the most famous was first known as the Primes.

What did the Primes change their name to before they became huge Motown stars?

    A.  The Temptations
    B.  The Miracles
    C.  The Four Tops

**ANSWER: A**
The Primes had all the talent they needed, but it wasn't until after they changed their name to the Temptations that the hits started coming. A side note: when the Supremes first came to Motown, they were called the Primettes, to compliment the Primes in the Motown stable of stars.

Detroit's Elmwood Cemetery is one of the oldest in Michigan. Among the names that appear on gravestones are Governor Lewis Cass, Revolutionary War veterans, and Civil War veterans, including 28 generals.

Other than being buried at Detroit's Elmwood Cemetery, what do Lucious Lyon, Thomas Palmer and Zahcariah Chandler have in common?

    A.  All were rumrunners during Prohibition.
    B.  All died in gunfights.
    C.  All were U.S. senators.

**ANSWER: C**
Lucious Lyon, Thomas Palmer, and Zachariah Chandler were all powerful U.S. senators representing Michigan. Another U.S. senator buried at Elmwood is Jacob Hart, credited with authoring the Thirteenth Amendment, which abolished slavery.

On October 2, 1873, 43 items were placed in a glass box and sealed in the cornerstone of the new Michigan state capitol building in Lansing.

What item was not included in the capitol cornerstone?

A. Lansing City Directory
B. Governor Mason's dentures
C. U.S. coins from 1873

**ANSWER: B**

Governor Stevens T. Mason's dentures were not sealed in the capitol cornerstone. When the box was opened in November of 1978, historians found the glass box smashed and full of wet ashes. The only things that survived were the coins.

"It's fresh as the dew from Kalamazoo" was an advertising slogan for an agricultural crop grown in Kalamazoo.

What was the Michigan crop that used that slogan?

A. Sweet corn
B. Celery
C. Sugar beets

**ANSWER: B**

In the 1860s, Dutch farmers took cheap swampland and transformed it into celery farms. After WWII, smaller farm families and scarce farm labor led to the end of the celery farms in the area. The celery farms ended up in California, where a less sweet variety of celery is grown.

The trumpeter swan is the largest native waterfowl in North America. It came close to extinction in Michigan.

What happened to the trumpeter swans?

A. They were killed by DDT poisoning.
B. They were killed for food by early settlers.
C. They were killed for quills and skins by Native Americans.

**ANSWER: C**

They were overhunted by Native Americans for quills and skin. Many experts believe they were gone before the first European settlers arrived.

What

Trumpeter swans have been reintroduced to the state from hatchlings produced at the Kellogg Bird Sanctuary in Battle Creek.

Auto Pioneer Henry Ford built a museum in Dearborn, Michigan, that contains buildings he collected, locomotives, planes, and an amazing array of artifacts.
What is the "official" name of the museum?

    A.  Henry Ford Museum
    B.  Greenfield Village
    C.  The Edison Institute

**ANSWER: C**
Greenfield Village and the Henry Ford Museum are "officially" the Edison Institute. Henry Ford named it after his good friend and hero Thomas Edison. Among its many artifacts, the museum houses what is believed to be Thomas Edison's last breath. The Edison Institute was dedicated on October 1, 1929.

In Michigan, there is a great diversity of life, large and small, fish and fowl.
What is the largest living thing in Michigan?

    A.  A giant mushroom
    B.  A white pine
    C.  A bull elk

**ANSWER: A**
Believe it or not, the largest living thing in Michigan is a giant mushroom. Scientists discovered the huge fungus growing near Crystal Falls in the early 1990s. The single mushroom covers more than 38 acres, is more than 1,500 years old, and is still growing! It may not be just the largest living thing in Michigan; it may be one of the oldest and largest living things on earth.

A geography question for all you map nuts: Caro, Michigan, is in the middle of the Thumb of Michigan and is the Tuscola county seat.
What was the original name of Caro?

    A.  Centerville

**What**

B.   Cairo

C.   Tuscola

**ANSWER: A**

Caro was first called Centerville because it was in the center of the Thumb. But when it came time to incorporate the village, it was discovered that there already was a Centerville, in St. Joseph County, so the folks there had to come up with another name. Influential businessman Will Sherman came up with the name Caro after looking at a map and noticing Cairo, Egypt. He dropped the *i*, and the rest is history.

---

The list of "official" things in the state of Michigan is large. Michigan has a state tree, rock, gem, flower, fossil, bird, and even fish. What is Michigan's official state fish?

A.   Bluegill

B.   Grayling

C.   Brook trout

**ANSWER: C**

Michigan's official state fish is the brook trout. Governor George Romney signed the bill that designated the brookie as the state fish in 1965. The legislation did not designate which kind of trout was to be the state fish, so the governor directed the state conservation office to decide.

---

The Michigan State Fair, based in Detroit, was the first in the country, founded in 1849. County fairs around the state soon sprang up. What is the oldest county fair in Michigan?

A.   Genesee County Fair

B.   Shiawassee County Fair

C.   Midland County Fair

**ANSWER: A**

The Genesee County Fair opened its gates for the first time in 1850. The first was held near the sawmills in downtown Flint. Jeremiah Smith, of Grand Blanc, was the first president of the Fair Board and led all the festivities.

What

There's not much left of the old stadium at the corner of Michigan Avenue and Trumbull Boulevard near Corktown in Detroit. Tiger Stadium was the home of the Detroit Tigers and major-league baseball from 1912 to 1999.

What name has NOT been the official name of Tiger Stadium over the years?

    A.  Briggs Stadium

    B.  Navin Field

    C.  Cobb's Corner

**ANSWER: C**
Though Ty Cobb is known as the greatest Tiger ever, Tiger Stadium was never known as Cobb's Corner. It was called Navin Field from 1912 to 1939, when owned by the Navin family, and Briggs Stadium from 1939 to 1961, when owned by the Briggs family. John Fetzer bought the team and gave the stadium a new name, Tiger Stadium, in 1961. It was also the home of the Detroit Lions from 1938 to 1974, when they moved to the Silverdome in Pontiac. Demolition of Tiger Stadium was completed on September 22, 2009. The Tigers now play in Comerica Park, named for a bank that paid to name the new park.

Many types of vessels have plied the waters of the Great Lakes. In 1942, the U.S. Navy christened a ship that would be the only one of its kind ever to sail the Great Lakes.

What kind of naval ship began to sail the Great Lakes in 1942?

    A.  Destroyer

    B.  Aircraft carrier

    C.  PT boat

**ANSWER: B**
The *USS Wolverine*, the first and only aircraft carrier ever to sail the Great Lakes, was commissioned in Chicago in August 1942 as a training vessel for aviators in WWII.

Herman "Germany" Schaefer has been called the greatest baseball player you've never heard of. The early Detroit Tiger played in the major leagues from 1901 to 1918 for the Chicago Orphans,

Detroit Tigers, Washington Senators, Newark Pepper, New York Yankees, and Cleveland Indians. One of his antics forced baseball to change its rules.

What did "Germany" Schaefer do that forced baseball to change its rules?

A. Took a chair to sit while playing outfield
B. Stole first base from second
C. Played barefoot

**ANSWER: B**

Herman A. "Germany" Schaefer was a fast runner who played from 1909 to 1918, including two World Series with the Tigers. Schaefer was a baseball trickster. One of his most famous exploits was stealing first base from second. With runners on first and third, a common ploy in baseball is the double steal to score the man on third. The idea is the runner stealing second draws a throw from the catcher as the runner on third steals home. But you have to have a man on first and third, so when the catcher did not throw the first time Schaefer stole second, he decided to steal first so they could make another attempt to score. According to legend, it worked the second time. In 1920, Major League Baseball outlawed stealing first.

A few place names, such as New York and Boston, have been given trademark status by the courts. There is one Michigan city that has a trademark on its name.

What Michigan city is also a registered trademark?

A. Grand Rapids
B. Mackinaw City
C. Grindstone City

**ANSWER: A**

Grand Rapids, Michigan, has been known as the furniture capital of the world for more than a century. Furniture makers in New Jersey, New York, and other places used the Grand Rapids name in their products to try to pick up business. In 1965, Macomb County Circuit Court awarded Grand Rapids trademark status for furniture.

Agriculture is big business in the Great Lakes: corn, soybeans, apples, peaches, and sugar beets all are major products produced in Great Lakes states.

What is Michigan's best-paying legal crop?

A. Sugar beets
B. Beans
C. Blueberries

**ANSWER: C**
Michigan's blueberry crop is the best-paying legal crop. While more money overall may be made in soybeans or sugar beets, farmers can make more per pint of blueberries. Michigan has more than 15,000 acres of blueberries, yielding 37–90 million pounds every year, at about 75 cents a pint.

Detroit Lions fans have been waiting a couple of generations for a championship team. But there is always hope. The year 1934 was big for the Lions.

What did the Lions do in 1934?

A. Lost their first game
B. Played their first game
C. Won their first game

**ANSWER: B, C**
In 1934, the Detroit Lions played their first game in the NFL at the University of Detroit stadium, and believe it or not, they won. They beat the New York Giants in front of 12,000 fans.

During WWII, Michigan was known as the arsenal of democracy. Once it changed over from the production of automobiles to war material, Michigan fed the Allies tons of equipment that helped to win the war. In September of 1942, the first weapon rolled off the line at Ford's Willow Run plant.

What was the first weapon to roll off the line at Willow Run in 1942?

A. Sherman tank
B. B-24 Liberator Bomber

C.  Thompson submachine gun

**ANSWER: B**
The first weapon to roll off the line at Ford's Willow Run plant was a B-24 Liberator Bomber. At peak production, the plant produced 18 a day! Over the course of the way, 8,500 were built at that plant to win the war.

Dreamers dream big, and for decades dreamers dreamed of a bridge to connect Michigan's Upper and Lower peninsulas. By the 1950s, engineers began to believe it could be done, but there were still skeptics.

What were the biggest concerns, of both builders and skeptics, about building the Mackinac Bridge?

A.  Ice floes
B.  Ships hitting the bridge
C.  Unstable bedrock

**ANSWER: A, B, C**
The big issues regarding the construction of the Mackinac Bridge were ice floes, unstable bedrock, and the possibility of ships hitting the great bridge. All the issues were dealt with, and today Big Mac is one of the longest bridges on earth.

Necessity is the mother of invention, the old saying goes, and that is especially true in the Great Lakes states. Something called a "Big Wheel" was invented in one of the Great Lakes states.

What is a "Big Wheel"?

A.  Children's bicycle
B.  Merry-go-round
C.  Log mover

**ANSWER: C**
In the Great Lakes states, lumbering was big business. In 1872, Silas Overpack, from Manistee, Michigan, invented the "Big Wheel" to move lumber in the spring and summer when the ground is soft and wet. Before the advent of Big Wheels, lumbering was done in winter so logs could be moved on sleighs to the rivers,

**What**

where they were floated to mills. The Big Wheel made lumbering a year-round venture throughout the Great Lakes.

When Alma College was founded in 1887, it had a four-person faculty. The positions included professors of math, physics, English-Latin-French, and mental and moral science.

What did that professor of mental and moral science teach?

A. Psychology
B. Philosophy
C. Animal husbandry

**ANSWER: B**
Reverend George Hunting was the first president of Alma College and the professor of mental and moral science, which is the study of philosophy.

Perhaps you've heard of Petoskey Stones, Grand Ledge, and Castle Rock.

What is the Ontonagon Boulder?

A. Kid Rock's backup band
B. A big piece of copper
C. A reef

**ANSWER: B**
The Ontonagon Boulder is a 3,700-pound mass of pure copper that was found on the bank of the Ontonagon River in Michigan's Upper Peninsula. As early as the seventeenth century, visitors to Lake Superior country were told of the boulder by Native Americans, who were said to leave offerings to the Great Spirit at the boulder. It was taken in 1843 by Julius Eldred to Detroit, Michigan, where it was confiscated by the War Department. It was then sent to Washington, D.C., and in 1860 was given to the Smithsonian Institution. That is where it remains today, though it is not on display because of its weight. They hope to display it in the future.

When Michigan was first being settled in the 1820s and 1830s, there was one commodity that was very valuable and very rare in Michigan.

What was it that early Michigan settlers needed but was hard to find?

A. Gold
B. Salt
C. Cotton

**ANSWER: B**

Early settlers might have longed for gold, but they needed salt, mostly to preserve meat. It is said that in the winter of 1846–1837 a fist-sized lump of salt could be traded for a 20-pound venison ham. It wasn't until the 1840s that salt began to be mined at places such as Saline, Michigan. Ironically, one of the largest salt mines in the world is under the city of Detroit.

In March of 1954, a new business opened that changed the country and landscape.

What was that business that changed the country in 1954?

A. A computer store
B. A mall
C. A cable television store

**ANSWER: B**

In March of 1954, Northland, the country's first shopping mall, opened in Southfield, Michigan. It was the beginning of a new era for shopping and downtowns.

The state of Michigan has enjoyed several population booms. One was brought on by the need for workers to build automobiles in the early twentieth century. The first big population boom in Michigan was in 1825.

What caused the population boom in Michigan in 1825?

A. The opening of the Flint and Pere Marquette Railroad
B. The opening of the Ohio Trail
C. The completion of the Erie Canal

**What**

**ANSWER: C**
With the completion of the Erie Canal, people began to come to Michigan by canal boat. The opening of the Sault Locks in 1855 completed the navigation system so large vessels could get to all parts of the Great Lakes.

The United States of America is separated from Europe by a vast ocean, so the nation has avoided conflicts that would have brought battles to our shores. Only one city in U.S. history was ever surrendered to a foreign enemy.
What was the only city in U.S. history to fall to a foreign power?

   A.  Mackinac Island, Michigan
   B.  Detroit, Michigan
   C.  Toledo, Michigan

**ANSWER: B**
In August of 1812, Territorial Governor William Hull surrendered Detroit to the British without firing a shot, during the War of 1812. The occupation lasted 13 months, but that gives Detroit the distinction of being the only city in U.S. history to surrender to a foreign enemy. By the way, Toledo was originally part of Michigan.

With 83 counties in Michigan, some are bigger than others. What Michigan county is the largest in land area?

   A.  Marquette County
   B.  Wayne County
   C.  Delta County

**ANSWER: A**
While Wayne County is the oldest county in the state and once included most of Michigan and parts of Wisconsin, Illinois, and Ohio, it is Marquette County that is Michigan's largest today. Marquette County, in the Upper Peninsula, has more than 1,841 square miles of area. That makes it more than 600 square miles larger than the state of Rhode Island.

People in the Great Lakes have always used slang to refer to everything from people and machines to places and animals.

What was it that Great Lakes residents called river hogs?

A. Sturgeon
B. Pigs in the water
C. Logs

**ANSWER: C**
"River hogs" were huge logs that lumbermen floated to sawmills.

---

Detroit has had many important industries over the centuries, from carriages and salt to carpet sweepers and wood stoves.

Before the turn of the twentieth century, what was the number one product made in Detroit?

A. Wheels for carriages
B. Cigars
C. Saddles

**ANSWER: B**
Before Detroit became the "Motor City," it was one of the leading manufacturers of cigars in the country. The first cigar factory in Detroit opened in 1840; the tobacco came mostly from Ontario, Canada, with some grown around Detroit. In 1969, the last cigar factory, the Scott Dillon Company, moved to Buffalo, New York, thus ending the cigar industry in Detroit.

---

The Detroit Tigers played baseball at the corner of Michigan and Trumbull for more than 100 years. The last game at Tiger Stadium was played in 1999. The first game was played at what was then Bennett Field on April 25, 1901.

What was on the site of Tiger Stadium before it was a baseball field?

A. A hay market
B. An onion farm
C. A fire station

**What**

**ANSWER: A**
The area that became Tiger Stadium was a hay market. To create the ball field, all they did was put 2 inches of dirt over the cobblestones that were left from the hay market.

---

In April of 1910, the Flint, Michigan, Police Department ordered a special piece of equipment for use by officers.

What was the equipment the Flint police ordered in 1910?

    A.  A paddy wagon

    B.  A police helmet

    C.  A siren for a horse and buggy

**ANSWER: A**
In 1910, the Flint Police Department asked the hometown Buick Motor Company to build the city's first paddy wagon. It had a 4 1/2 × 6 1/2 cage mounted on the bed and had curtains that could be pulled to keep prisoners from public view.

---

In 1846, the state of Michigan became the first state in the union and the first government in the Western world to ban the death penalty, with one exception

What is the one reason that Michigan would allow the death penalty?

    A.  Kidnapping a child

    B.  Murder of the governor or a legislator

    C.  Treason

**ANSWER: C**
The only crime that is punishable by death is treason.

---

Over the years, people have done some wild things on the Mackinac Bridge. In May of 1988, something brand new happened on the Big Mac.

What happened on the Mackinac Bridge for the first time in 1983?

    A.  A baby was born.

B. A wedding took place.

C. Someone stopped for an oil change.

**ANSWER: A**

A Chippewa County woman gave birth on the bridge as her car crossed on the way to a Petoskey hospital. An ambulance arrived in time to help with the delivery in the middle of Big Mac.

When Michigan's new state capital was moved from Detroit to Lansing, one critic said the area was "just a hole in the woods." The state legislature already had a name for the new capital.

What did the legislature first call the state's new capital city?

A. Centerline

B. Michigan

C. Lansing Township

**ANSWER: B**

The legislature called the new city Michigan, Michigan. The city had been carved out of Lansing Township, so when common sense suggested that it would be confusing to call the city Michigan, they changed their minds and renamed the city after the township.

In the 1870s, people all over Michigan who had been in good health began to get sick. They were suffering from headaches, bronchitis, weight loss and more, and nobody knew why.

What caused this mystery illness in the 1870s?

A. Wallpaper

B. Moonshine whiskey

C. Horseflies

**ANSWER: A**

The mystery illness was brought on by green wallpaper. The green pigment was called Paris green, and it was made with arsenic. The people in Michigan in the 1870s were suffering from arsenic poisoning. It took several years before Dr. Robert C. Kedsie, a professor at Michigan Agricultural College (later MSU), figured it out.

**What**

Once upon a time in Michigan, there was a place called Wenona Beach near Bay City.
What was Wenona Beach known for?

A. A campground
B. An amusement park
C. A shipyard

**ANSWER: B**
Wenona Beach was an amusement park in Bay City that operated from 1897 until it closed in 1964. Wenona Beach was actually the original name for West Bay City, but in 1905, the city annexed it. The name Wenona was from the famous Longfellow poem "The Song of Hiawatha." Wenona is the name of Hiawatha's mother.

By 1879, the city of Detroit was a major city, the seventeenth-largest city in the country. Even though it was a big city, Detroit had to pass a law to outlaw a common practice.
What did the Detroit City Council outlaw in 1897?

A. Target shooting
B. Camping
C. Pasturing cattle

**ANSWER: C**
The city of Detroit had to pass an ordinance forbidding the running of large cattle in public places. Of course, people protested. Don't try to run cattle in Detroit today; the law is still on the books.

Customers used to go to the counter at a store and tell the clerk what they wanted, and the clerk would get it for them. Now we go to places such as A&P, grab a shopping cart, and pick up the stuff for ourselves.
What does A&P stand for?

A. Apples & Pears
B. Anderson & Prescott
C. Atlantic & Pacific

**ANSWER: C**
A&P stands for Atlantic & Pacific. The full name of the company that runs A&P stores is the Great Atlantic & Pacific Tea Company.

The city of Detroit is more than 300 years old, one of the oldest cities in America.

What is the only entity that still exists that dates back to the founding of Detroit in 1701?

    A.  The Detroit Fire Department
    B.  St. Anne's Church
    C.  The *Detroit Free Press*

**ANSWER: B**
St. Anne's Church was founded on July 26, 1701, 48 hours after Antoine de la Mothe Cadillac landed in Detroit and began to build a fort. It is the only organization that still exists 300 years later.

John Lennon said that without Elvis, there wouldn't be rock 'n' roll. Elvis has a Michigan connection.

What is Elvis's connection to Michigan?

    A.  His manager was born in Michigan.
    B.  He first performed in Michigan.
    C.  His first hit was written by a man who lived in Michigan.

**ANSWER: C**
Elvis Presley's first hit, "Heartbreak Hotel," was written by steel guitarist Thomas Durden. He played in the backup bands of Johnny Cash and Tex Ritter, among others. He achieved rock 'n' roll immortality for coauthoring "Heartbreak Hotel," Elvis Presley's first RCA Victor single to chart nationally. Durden was born in Georgia but was raised in Florida, and later he lived in Houghton Lake, Michigan.

Shipping on the Great Lakes is a major industry employing thousands to move tons of cargo from all over the world.

What was the first known European vessel to sail the Great Lakes?

**What**

A. The *Nina*
B. The *Griffon*
C. The *S. R. Heddy*

**ANSWER: B**

The *Griffon* was built at Niagara Falls in 1679. In August, it sailed across Lake Erie to Detroit. It was last seen on September 7, 1679. No one knows what became of the 50-ton ship.

The *Nina* was one of Christopher Columbus's ships of discovery.

The *S. R. Heddy* is not a ship but the names of two of the author's best friends, Steve and Rosanne Heddy. The Heddys own a painting and decorating company and are community activists in Flint. They are founders of Operation Brush-Up, a project that restored hundreds of homes using thousands of volunteers, and they serve on numerous boards and projects.

On July 4, 1983, two daredevils were arrested for doing something wild in downtown Detroit.

What did those daredevils do?

A. Climb the Renaissance Center
B. Jump from the Ambassador Bridge
C. Skydive into Tiger Stadium

**ANSWER: A**

Two climbers took their climbing equipment and scaled the 73-story Westin Hotel, today the Marriott. It took them 6 1/2 hours to get to the top, where they were immediately arrested.

Earthquakes are rare in Michigan, but they do happen. There have been some 35 documented earthquakes since the first was reported by French missionaries in 1663.

What do researchers believe is the cause of most of Michigan's earthquakes?

A. Movement along fault lines
B. Human activity
C. Severe weather

**ANSWER: B**

According to a Department of Natural Resources report in 1977, only three or four of Michigan's earthquakes were caused by seismic faults. The rest were caused by human activity such as mining, train wrecks, and collapsing mines.

Michigan often has steamy weather in the summer. It can get pretty hot—not as hot as Arizona or California but still hot.

What is the highest temperature ever recorded in Michigan?

    A.  108
    B.  112
    C.  117

**ANSWER: B**

On July 13, 1936, a high temperature reading of 112 degrees Fahrenheit was recorded at Mio.

Many organizations are known by a nickname; an example is the Y for the YMCA.

What is the common name of the Order of the Patrons of Husbandry?

    A.  The Masons
    B.  The Whigs
    C.  The Grange

**ANSWER: C**

The Order of the Patrons of Husbandry is better known as the Grange. The Grange is the nation's oldest national agricultural organization, with 300,000 members. It had units established in 3,600 local communities in 37 states. It was formed in the years following the American Civil War. There were many Granges in communities all over the Great Lakes states. You can still find Grange signs at old halls around the country.

On April 3, 1961, newspapers all over the state of Michigan bore headlines that declared "Con Con Approved," a headline that both excited and worried Michiganians.

What was Con Con?

A. A constitutional convention

B. A new prison

C. A banned dance

**ANSWER: A**

"Con Con" was what the Michigan Constitutional Convention of 1961 was called. George Romney, an automotive executive, led the convention and made enough of a name for himself that he would soon be elected governor of Michigan.

Many laws passed by city councils and legislatures have come and gone. Sometimes the need for a law goes away, and often morals of the day force a change in laws. Sometimes those laws that are no longer on the books leave a memory, such as the "blue laws."

What were the blue laws?

A. Women had to wear blue hats on Sundays

B. Alcohol sales were regulated

C. Musicians could not play the blues on Sundays

**ANSWER: B**

Blue laws referred to laws that prohibited the sale and use of alcohol. One memory of blue laws in Michigan is the fact that it is still illegal to buy alcohol on Sunday mornings before noon.

Dolls are a classic children's toy, especially for little girls. Dolls such as Chatty Cathy, Beanie Babies, and Barbie have been loved by children for years.

What famous doll was first manufactured in Michigan?

A. Barbie

B. Raggedy Ann

C. G. I. Joe

**ANSWER: B**

Raggedy Ann was created in 1918 by a political cartoonist and illustrator named Johnny Gruelle. She was manufactured by two companies in Muskegon: the Nonbreakable Toy Company and the Muskegon Toy and Garment Works.

Oldsmobile was the oldest of the auto nameplates at its demise in 2002. It was founded by Ransom E. Olds in 1897. Mr. Olds left the company he named for himself in 1904 to found the REO Company. Olds named the company REO for two reasons. First, the letters "REO" were his initials.

What was the second reason Ransom Olds named his new auto company REO?

    A.  Rio de Janeiro
    B.  REO-rganization
    C.  Greek for "to run"

**ANSWER: C**
"Reo" is also Greek for "to run," something you hope your car always does.

One of the biggest college football rivalries in the nation is the annual University of Michigan–Michigan State University clash. In that game, they play for bragging rights and a trophy.

What is the name of the trophy the Wolverines and Spartans play for each fall?

    A.  The Paul Bunyan Trophy
    B.  The Heisman Trophy
    C.  The Little Brown Jug

**ANSWER: A**
Since 1953, the Spartans and the Wolverines have played for the Paul Bunyan Trophy. The awarding of the 4-foot-high symbol was begun by Michigan Governor G. Mennen Williams.

The Seven Wonders of the World were a list of seven ancient sites, such as the Sphinx and the pyramids, first described in a poem composed about 140 BC by Antipater of Sidon. Philo of Byzantium, Herodotus, and others later listed their versions of the Seven Wonders of the Ancient World. Today, writers and travelers continue to create their own Seven Wonders.

**What**

What Michigan site was once called one of the Seven Wonders of the World?

A. The Mackinac Bridge
B. The Willow Run plant
C. The Windsor Tunnel

**ANSWER: B**
In 1942, Henry Ford opened his Willow Run plant to build bombers for the WWII war effort. It was the largest factory on earth, with more than 2.5 million square feet of floor space.

Everything in Frankenmuth, Michigan, one of the top tourist destinations in the Great Lakes, is based on a Bavarian theme—everything, that is, except Zehnders Restaurant.
What is Zehnders Restaurant designed to look like?

A. The Capitol
B. Buckingham Palace
C. Mount Vernon

**ANSWER: C**
Zehnders Restaurant was built to look like George Washington's Mount Vernon home. The restaurant was built in the 1920s before Frankenmuth began to transform itself into a Bavarian village tourist attraction.

Show business brings talented people from all over the country, and Michigan has its share of stars. Amos Yakhoob was a very famous television star for many years, and he was born in Michigan.
What was the stage name Amos Yakhoob Jacobs used as a star of radio and television?

A. Danny Thomas
B. Sonny Bono
C. Jack Parr

**ANSWER: A**
Amos Yakhoob was the real name of television star Danny Thomas, famous for his sitcom *Make Room for Daddy* and known for his famous daughter, Marlo.

He is also the founder of the St. Jude's Children's Research Hospital. He was born in Deerfield, Michigan.

Auto exports have been big business for Michigan's auto industry. Vehicles are shipped to all points of the globe.
What country received the first U.S. auto export?

A. England
B. Canada
C. India

ANSWER: C

The first known auto export from the United States was a steam vehicle exported to India. It was built by Ransom Olds in 1893.

What Michigan-born actress won an Academy Award?

A. Kim Hunter
B. Ellen Burstyn
C. Lily Tomlin

ANSWER: A

Kim Hunter was born Janet Cole in Detroit in 1922. She originated the roll of Stella in the Broadway production of *A Streetcar Named Desire* and won a best supporting actress Oscar and a Golden Globe for the same role in the 1951 film version. Kim Hunter died at age 79 in 2002.

What supermodel was born in Michigan?

A. Kathy Ireland
B. Nikki Taylor
C. Christie Brinkley

ANSWER: C

Supermodel Christie Brinkley was born on February 2, 1953, in Monroe, Michigan.

**What**

Once upon a time, a bark spud would have been very common in Michigan. Your great-grandparents might have used it.
What is a bark spud?

A. A kind of light beer
B. A tool for trees
C. A potato

**ANSWER: B**
A bark spud was used to strip bark from logs so that people could collect tannin, which is used to treat animal hides.

Some of the biggest names in show business got their start in Vaudeville. Vaudeville was known for its live variety shows touring the United States and Canada between the early 1880s and the 1930s. Bob Hope, Bing Crosby, Milton Berle, and George Burns all got their start in Vaudeville. There is a Michigan connection.
What Michigan city became a Mecca for vacationing Vaudeville stars?

A. Muskegon
B. Traverse City
C. Monroe

**ANSWER: A**
In 1903, Vaudevillians began to go to Muskegon's Bluffton District to enjoy the lake breeze. The great comedian Buster Keaton wrote that as a child, his family's home in Muskegon was the only home they ever owned.

Michigan is known for its drives, among many other things.
What kind of drives were Michigan residents first known for?

A. Cattle drives
B. Log drives
C. Sunday drives

**ANSWER: B**
While a Sunday drive is nice and Michigan has had its share of cattle drives, the biggest drives were log drives during Michigan's lumber era. By the mid-1800s,

lumbermen were using Michigan's rivers to get their logs to the sawmills. Lumberjacks rode and herded them down the river on their "log drives."

There are a number of early radio shows that became television shows as well.

What Detroit radio show later became a hit TV show?

A. The Lone Ranger
B. Dragnet
C. The Edge of Night

**ANSWER: A**

The Detroit radio show that became a hit TV show was *The Lone Ranger*. It went on the air in January of 1933 on WXYZ. It later made Clayton Moore and Jay Silverheels stars as the Lone Ranger and his loyal sidekick, Tonto.

In December of 1837, a gathering of politicians took place in Ann Arbor, Michigan. That meeting has been called "the Frostbitten Convention."

What was decided at the Frostbitten Convention?

A. Michigan's first U.S. Senator was appointed.
B. The Toledo Compromise
C. The establishment of a weather bureau

**ANSWER: B**

The Frostbitten Convention was called to settle the dispute with Ohio over Toledo. In 1836, delegates had rejected the Toledo Compromise, which would have given the Upper Peninsula to Michigan in exchange for Toledo. In December 1837, they met again in a very cold Ann Arbor, and this time they agreed to give up claims to Toledo in exchange for the U.P. so Michigan could enter the union as a state.

James Vernor was a pharmacist in Detroit who created the soft drink that he called Vernor's ginger ale. When asked, James Vernor said that one thing was responsible for the creation of his famous drink.

What did James Vernor say was responsible for his discovery of the unique taste of his soda?

**What**

A. Detroit River water
B. The Civil War
C. Mincemeat pie

**ANSWER: B**
Vernor had been a pharmacist before the Civil War. When he went off to fight the war, he left ginger and other ingredients in an oak cask for almost four years. When he returned, he found that he had made the first Vernor's ginger ale syrup. By 1866, he was in the business of making Vernor's. It's still aged in oak casks to this day.

Henry Ford is a legendary figure around the world. He is known for creating the Model T, building a huge museum, and creating a corporation that bears his name 100 years later.

What did Henry Ford do that first brought him worldwide attention?

A. Experimented with soybeans
B. Created the assembly line
C. Paid $5 a day to his workers

**ANSWER: C**
While experimenting with soybeans and the assembly line were major innovations, it was the shocking idea of paying his employees $5 a day that first brought him worldwide attention.

Ford was one of America's foremost soybean and soyfood pioneers. He developed many new ways to use the crop industrially and was one of the most creative of the original soy foods pioneers.

Freeways changed the way we live in America. They made commuting possible, helped make our society much more mobile, and brought down costs to bring products to market.

What city had the first interchange of two freeways?

A. Los Angeles
B. Detroit
C. Grand Rapids

ANSWER: C
In 1964, the city of Grand Rapids, Michigan, became the first city in the country to have an interchange in its downtown when I-196 and US 131 were built.

In 1879, a Michigan State University professor began an experiment that is now the longest ongoing science experiment in history. What is the subject of that experiment?

A. Elephants' life spans
B. Seeds of weeds
C. Temperature fluctuation

ANSWER: B
Dr. William Beal was a professor of botany at what was then Michigan Agricultural College. He buried 20 one-point bottles of seeds of common weeds. One is dug up every 10 years to see whether it will still grow. Dr. Beal's experiment will continue until the year 2040.

As the home of the auto industry, Michigan has been building roads to run cars on for more than a century. There is only one road in the state—perhaps in the nation—that has never had an auto accident. What road has never had an auto accident?

A. M-185
B. M-21
C. M-55

ANSWER: A
The only state road in Michigan, and maybe the country, that has never had an auto accident is M-185. That's not too much of a surprise because M-185 is the road that circles Mackinac Island. By law, there are no automobiles allowed on Mackinac Island. However, there have been some very serious bicycle accidents on that road.

One of the oldest cities in the country is Sault Ste. Marie, Michigan, sometimes called the Soo. It is on the border with Canada in Michigan's Upper Peninsula. It was founded as a mission in 1668 by Father Jacques Marquette.

**What**

What does the "Sault" mean in Sault Ste. Marie?

A. A salt lick
B. A cascade
C. An Indian tribe

**ANSWER: B**
The "Sault" in Sault Ste. Marie is a French word that refers to the cascades or rapids in the St. Marie River that connects Lake Superior with the lower Great Lakes.

Michigan is known for its forests, lakes, and streams. It is a wonderful place to visit if you like outdoor beauty.

Other than the fact that they are both parks, what do New York's Central Park and Detroit, Michigan's, Belle Isle have in common?

A. Both are on waterfronts.
B. They were designed by the same person.
C. They were the first parks to be built by a state.

**ANSWER: B**
Both New York's famous Central Park and Detroit's Belle Isle were designed by renowned architect Fredrick Law Olmstead. They were also the first paid for by local citizens. Olmstead is considered the father of American landscape architecture. He designed many well-known urban parks, including Presque Isle Park in Marquette, Michigan; the Grand Necklace of Parks in Milwaukee, Wisconsin; Marquette Park in Chicago; and the landscape surrounding the U.S. Capitol building.

The Wayne County Courthouse in Detroit was built in 1897. It is a beautiful building with many artistic features. One of those features is a 40-foot-wide stairway with a storage space underneath that contains a mystery.

What was that space under the stairs designed to store?

A. Hay for horses
B. Court records
C. Bicycles

One of Michigan's favorite sons is Gerald R. Ford, a former Michigan football player, a congressman, and the only person from Michigan to serve as president of the United States. He also coauthored a book in 1965.

What was the name of President Gerald Ford's book?

    A.   Portrait of an Assassin

    B.   Under the Helmet

    C.   Golf for Politicians

The Soo Locks are the waterway that opens Lake Superior to the lower lakes. They are also a big tourist attraction. Many have watched as freighters slide though the locks.

What is the official name of the Soo Locks?

    A.   Soo Locks

    B.   Ste. Mary's Falls Canal

    C.   Sault Ste. Marie Locks

Over the years, people have picked up nicknames by where they are from. A couple of examples: youpers are from the Upper Peninsula, and trolls are from under the Mackinac Bridge.

What is an "island goat"?

**What**

A. A sheep farmer
B. A Drummond Island native
C. A veteran sailor

**ANSWER: C**
An "island goat" is a Great Lakes sailor who has participated in at least 25 Mackinac sail races.

The Great Lakes region's second-biggest industry was lumbering after the fur trade ran out. Like most industries, there were slang terms used for job titles. English majors likely would call these words the "lexicon" of the industry. Back then, a "lumberjack" was anyone who cut wood, and a "river rat" guided logs down the river to the sawmill.

What was a "woodpecker"?

A. Someone who picked logs for mills
B. A poor wood cutter
C. A log thief

**ANSWER: B**
Real lumberjacks called the guys who were not good wood cutters "woodpeckers" because they just pecked at the logs.

There are many kinds of schools, colleges, universities, elementary schools, secondary schools, and normal schools.

What is a "normal school"?

A. A school where the students are normal
B. A school where special-needs students were educated in the late 1800s
C. A school to train teachers

**ANSWER: C**
A normal school trained high school graduates to be teachers. Its name came from its purpose, to establish teaching standards or norms. Eastern Michigan University was Michigan's first normal school.

What Michigan city is situated at the highest point in the Lower Peninsula?

   A.  Gaylord
   B.  Holland
   C.  Kingston

**ANSWER: A**
The highest point in the Lower Peninsula is Gaylord. The city in northern Michigan used its elevation to its advantage when it became the "Alpine Village" of Michigan. Gaylord has many golf courses and ski resorts to attract tourists year round.

The Great Lakes are an important shipping route to the entire Midwest. The only problem is that the lakes freeze over in the winter, thus stopping all shipping.

    In what year did shipping continue on the Great Lakes for the entire year—or has that never happened?

   A.  1879
   B.  1975
   C.  It never happened.

**ANSWER: B**
In April of 1975, a Canadian tanker fought its way through the Soo Locks to complete a full year of shipping on the Great Lakes.

The Detroit Tigers Baseball Club has been playing baseball for more than a century. During that period, the team has won several games by forfeit. There is one team that the Tigers have beat twice by forfeit.

    What major-league baseball team has lost to the Detroit Tigers twice by forfeit?

   A.  New York Yankees
   B.  Washington Senators
   C.  Chicago White Sox

**ANSWER: C**
The Tigers have won two games over the Chicago White Sox by forfeit: a game in 1907 when the Sox were delaying the game in hopes of getting a rainout and the infamous Disco Demolition Night, July 12, 1979, at Comiskey Park in Chicago. It was held between games of a twi-night doubleheader. Led by local DJ Steve Dahl, rowdy fans surged onto the field, and a near riot ensued. The umpires called the game, and the commissioner awarded the forfeit win to the Tigers.

The Great Lakes states have always been a place for hunting and fishing. Michigan has herds of large animals, including deer and elk.

What large animals were common in Michigan and the Great Lakes states in the 1600s?

    A. Buffalo/bison
    B. Elk
    C. Sheep

**ANSWER: A**
The American bison, often called the buffalo, was common throughout the nation, from Montana to Florida. At one time, there were more bison in Michigan than deer and elk.

What Michigan city has three rivers running through it?

    A. Grand Rapids
    B. Lansing
    C. Escanaba

**ANSWER: B**
Lansing has three rivers flowing through it: the Red Cedar, the Grand River, and the Sycamore.

Pitching, they say, is the lifeblood of baseball. Good pitching beats good hitting anytime. The Detroit Tigers have had some great pitchers over the years, but only one won two Cy Young Awards in a row.

What Tiger pitcher won two Cy Young Awards in a row?

    A. Denny McClain
    B. "Schoolboy" Rowe

C.  Jack Morris

**ANSWER: A**

Denny McClain won two Cy Young Awards: in 1968, when he won 31 games, and in 1969, when he won 27. He also spent time in prison for drug trafficking, embezzlement, and racketeering.

Lynwood "Schoolboy" Rowe pitched for the Tigers from 1932 to 1942. Jack Morris played in 18 seasons, mainly for the Detroit Tigers, and won 254 games. He was the winningest pitcher of the 1980s and played in four World Series championships.

We are familiar with David Buick. He was an auto pioneer and mechanic who, along with Billy Durant, built Buick Motors. He is also credited with another invention.

What other well-known appliance was David Buick known for?

A.  Lawn sprinkler
B.  Rubber horseshoes
C.  Windshield wipers

**ANSWER: A**

David Buick, the founder of Buick Motors, was a plumber by trade and invented the lawn sprinkler in about 1882. He also created a way to coat cast iron with enamel so bathtubs could be less expensive.

Michigan is the Great Lakes State, and it does have a lot of lakes. But one Michigan city is on three lakes.

What city in Michigan is set on three lakes?

A.  Houghton Lake
B.  Charlevoix
C.  Holland

**ANSWER: B**

Charlevoix, named after Pierre François Xavier de Charlevoix, a French explorer, is situated on three lakes: Lake Michigan, Lake Charlevoix, and Round Lake.

**What**

Many believe that after the Revolutionary War, the English pulled out of the United States, but that is not true. They lingered until after the War of 1812.

What Michigan fort was the last encampment of British troops in the United States?

    A.  Fort Wayne

    B.  Fort Mackinac

    C.  Fort Drummond

**ANSWER: C**

Fort Drummond was built on Drummond Island, off the shore of the Upper Peninsula, after the War of 1812. It wasn't until 1822 that the British finally left and returned to Canada.

An increased security presence at airports, power plants, and public buildings is now the norm. During WWII, security was also very high.

What was the most heavily guarded site in the United States during WWII?

    A.  The White House

    B.  The Ford Willow Run plant

    C.  The Soo Locks

**ANSWER: C**

The most heavily guarded site in the United States during WWII was the Soo Locks. They were important because the locks are the only route to bring iron from Lake Superior country to the rest of the nation.

WWI American flying ace Eddie Rickenbacker was America's first flying ace, having shot down 26 enemy aircraft. He earned the Medal of Honor and 10 Distinguished Flying Crosses. After the war, Rickenbacker lived in Detroit.

What did flying ace Eddie Rickenbacker do after the war?

    A.  Founded a car company

    B.  Commanded the Michigan National Guard

    C.  Taught

ANSWER: A
Eddie Rickenbacker founded the Rickenbacker Motor Company. He had been a race car driver before the war, competing against the likes of David Buick and Louis Chevrolet. His company went bankrupt in 1927. Rickenbacker later became president of Eastern Airlines and owned the Indianapolis Motor Speedway. He died at age 82 in 1973.

Michigan enjoys many different natural environments: rivers, lakes, forests, swamps, prairies, and even mountains.
What of the following is not a mountain range in Michigan?

    A.  Porcupine Mountains
    B.  Huron Mountains
    C.  Keweenaw Mountains
    D.  Superior Mountains

ANSWER: D
There is no such thing as the Superior Mountains. But there are the Huron Mountains, mostly in Marquette and Baraga counties. Their highest peak, Mount Arvon, is the highest point in Michigan.
    The Keweenaw Mountains are on the Keweenaw Peninsula. The Porcupine Mountains, or Porkies, are in Ontonagon and Gogebic counties. All of Michigan's mountains are in the U.P. and overlook Lake Superior.

Americans have been flying into orbit since John Glenn Jr. orbited the Earth three times on February 20, 1962, in his *Friendship 7* ship. Since then, there have been many flights into orbit and to the moon. But over those years, only one college logo has been seen aboard a spaceship.
    What college logo was broadcast from space during the voyage of the space shuttle *Columbia* in 1982?

    A.  University of Michigan
    B.  Stanford University
    C.  MIT

ANSWER: A
In March of 1982, Colonel Jack Lousma, a Michigan grad, pointed a camera at the maize and blue "M-Go Blue" bumper sticker aboard the shuttle *Columbia*.

**What**

Shipping is important to the economies of nations all over the world, and rivers have always been the highways for goods to be delivered.

What river handles more shipping than any other in the world?

A.  Thames
B.  Mississippi
C.  Detroit
D.  Saginaw

**ANSWER: C**

The Detroit River is the busiest shipping lane in the world, with all the traffic on the Great Lakes funneled though it.

Private eyes have been a television staple since the early days of broadcast. From *77 Sunset Strip* to *Dragnet* and *NYPD Blue*, Americans love their cop shows.

What TV private eye is from Michigan?

A.  Tom Selleck
B.  James Garner
C.  Mike Conners
D.  Mike Spencer

**ANSWER: A**

Tom Selleck, television's Magnum, P.I., was born in Detroit on January 29, 1955.

James Garner was the star of *The Rockford Files*, and Mike Conners was television's Mannix.

Michael R. Spencer is not a private eye or a cop, but he is one of the leading financial advisors in the state of Michigan. The Flint native is the father of three and the author of two books. Mike created a foundation to help orphans in Thailand and is the founder of Next Michigan, a conference facility promoting the vitality and entrepreneurial spirit of Michigan.

Lumberjacks had a very colorful vocabulary. Many words they used cannot be used in so-called polite company. Some of the slang terms used by lumberjacks were very colorful and descriptive.

What did the lumbermen call a "Michigan cackleberry"?

A.  Fruit farmer turned politician

What

B. Egg

C. Poison ivy

**ANSWER: B**

A "Michigan cackleberry" was what chicken eggs were called in lumber camps.

Airport abbreviations are used to identify the city where baggage and people are bound. Some are easy, such as FNT for Flint, Michigan, and MBS for Midland, Bay City, and Saginaw. The designation for Chicago's O'Hare Airport is ORD.

What does the ORD abbreviation stand for at Chicago's O'Hare Airport?

A. O'Hare Radio Designation

B. Orchard Field

C. John P. Orday

**ANSWER: B**

The original name of Chicago's O'Hare Airport was Orchard Field because it was built in an orchard. When the airport was renamed in honor of navy pilot Edward "Butch" O'Hare in 1949, they kept the original abbreviation, ORD. O'Hare was born in 1914, the son of a wealthy businessman and attorney. In 1939, his father was gunned down by Al Capone's gunmen. He probably had given the government information useful in its prosecution of Capone. In February 1942, O'Hare was awarded the Congressional Medal of Honor for saving his ship, the *Lexington*. He was shot down in November of 1943 by enemy fire.

Michigan's state flag has symbols of the state and the Latin words *Si quaeris peninsulam amoenam, circumspice* ("If you seek a pleasant peninsula, look about you"), the state motto. The flag also has images of three animals.

What animal is not on the Michigan state flag?

A. Elk

B. Bald eagle

C. Wolverine

**ANSWER: C**

The Michigan state flag has an eagle, an elk, and even a moose, but there is no wolverine to be found.

In 1783, the Northwest Territory, including the Great Lakes, became part of the United States.

What treaty made the Northwest Territory part of the United States?

- A. Treaty of Paris
- B. Treaty of Saginaw
- C. Treaty of Versailles

**ANSWER: A**

The Treaty of Paris, negotiated by Secretary of State Thomas Jefferson, gave the Northwest Territory to the United States.

The Treaty of Versailles ended WWI, and the Treaty of Saginaw was a deal to take land for the Native Americans.

Michigan is a very large state. It can take many hours to go from one end of the state to another.

What city is the farthest from Detroit?

- A. Washington, D.C.
- B. Copper Harbor, Michigan
- C. St. Louis, Missouri

**ANSWER: B**

Copper Harbor, Michigan, in the Upper Peninsula is the farthest from Detroit. St. Louis, Missouri, is almost 400 miles from Detroit, and Washington, D.C., is 550 miles from Detroit, but Copper Harbor, Michigan, is almost 600 miles from Detroit.

What did Julius Ropes discover in Michigan in 1881?

- A. Diamonds
- B. Gold
- C. The Porcupine Mountains

**ANSWER: B**

Ropes, a chemist and geologist from Marquette, discovered gold near Ishpeming in the Upper Peninsula. He began a mining operation in 1883 and dug more than $700,000 in gold before closing it in 1897.

Holly, Michigan, is known for its Carry Nation Festival. The festival is named for the famous temperance advocate who came to Holly on August 28, 1908, to destroy saloons. She came to "Battle Alley" wielding her umbrella and hatchet as she smashed through the alley's bars and bellowed about the "Demon rum" and its sin.

How did Battle Alley get its name?

A. Because of the Carry Nation Battle
B. It was named for city founder George Battle.
C. Because of a big fight between locals and a traveling circus

**ANSWER: C**

Battle Alley was the scene of many brawls, but the most famous may be when Carry Nation came to town to smash the bars. However, it was actually named after a fight with locals and a traveling circus in 1880.

"Win one for the Gipper" was a famous line spoken by Ronald Reagan as Notre Dame football star George Gipp in the film *Knute Rockne All American*. George Gipp was from Laurium, Michigan, in the Upper Peninsula.

What connection did George Gipp have to Flint?

A. He played semipro ball there.
B. He worked at Buick.
C. His parents came from Flint.

**ANSWER: B**

George Gipp worked at the Buick factory in 1919 after he got kicked out of Notre Dame. He worked there until he was allowed to return to Notre Dame for his senior season in 1920. Gipp died at the age of 25 of streptococcal throat infection, days after leading Notre Dame to a win over Northwestern.

In Michigan, you are never far from one of the Great Lakes.

What is the farthest you can be from one of the Great Lakes if you are in Michigan?

- A. 30 miles
- B. 85 miles
- C. 123 miles

**ANSWER: B**
In Michigan, you are never more than 85 miles from one of the big lakes.

Chain saws have taken over the job that axes once did, but there are still several styles of axes that are available.

What is a Michigan ax?

- A. An ax shaped like Michigan
- B. An ax made in Michigan City, Indiana
- C. A double-bitted ax

**ANSWER: C**
The Michigan ax is a double-bitted ax, meaning it has a blade on both sides. It was proven to be more aerodynamic and easier to use for lumberjacks felling the great forests of the Great Lakes.

In 1978, an event was held in Detroit that hadn't happened before and hasn't happened since.

What event took place in 1978 that hasn't been repeated?

- A. Bullfight
- B. Elephant roundup
- C. Octopus hunt

**ANSWER: A**
In September 1978, more than 4,000 people went to Cobo Hall in Detroit to see a bloodless bullfight. To win, the matador had to put a rose between the bull's horns instead of killing him.

A big party took place in September 1981 in Grand Rapids, Michigan. Bob Hope, Sammy Davis Jr., Speaker "Tip" O'Neill,

Danny Thomas, and Presidents Ronald Reagan and Gerald Ford were among the glittering assemblage.

What was that party celebrating?

A. Michigan's sesquicentennial
B. Grand Rapids' centennial
C. A museum dedication

**ANSWER: C**

That group of VIPs was in Grand Rapids to dedicate the Gerald R. Ford Presidential Museum.

In October of 1871, what many consider Michigan's greatest disaster began.

What happened in October 1871?

A. A fire
B. A ship sank
C. Banks closed

**ANSWER: A**

In October 1871, the same day that Mrs. O'Leary's cow was supposed to have started the Great Chicago Fire, fires also started along Michigan's west shore of Lake Michigan. Fanned by high winds and fed by the scraps left from the lumber industry, the fires swept across the entire state to Lake Huron. In the Thumb, 90% of the homes were destroyed. Holland and Manistee were all but wiped off the map. Hundreds died, and thousands were left homeless. It was also the first time the American Red Cross responded to a disaster.

What Michigan county is named for a man who was hung as a traitor to his country?

A. Wayne
B. Emmet
C. Houghton

**ANSWER: B**

Emmet County, at the very tip of Lower Michigan, was named for Robert Emmet, an Irish patriot who was hung by the British in 1803 as a traitor.

**What**

Michigan has many rivers. One was first known as "the River of the Black Robe."
What Michigan river was called the River of the Black Robe?

    A.  Rifle River

    B.  Black River

    C.  Pere Marquette River

**ANSWER: C**

The Pere Marquette River was first called the River of the Black Robe by both the Native Americans and the first Europeans in the state. It was so called because that is where Father Jacques Marquette died and was first buried.

Auto pioneer Henry Ford had his hand in many products besides cars. Many products are very familiar to us today, though most are not associated with Mr. Ford.
What product did Henry Ford invent?

    A.  Charcoal briquettes

    B.  Premium gasoline

    C.  Microwave ovens

**ANSWER: A**

Henry Ford was among the first to understand the value of recycling and created the charcoal briquettes from wood left over from shipping crates.

What city is the farthest east?

    A.  Detroit, Michigan

    B.  Port Huron, Michigan

    C.  Atlanta, Georgia

**ANSWER: B**

Port Huron is farther east than Atlanta, Georgia, and Detroit. Some other interesting geographic notes: Hancock, Michigan, is farther north than Montreal, Canada, and Ironwood, Michigan, is farther west than St. Louis, Missouri.

**What**

Michigan is known for many crops and a large number of fruit trees, such as cherry, apple, and pear trees.

What fruit tress are likely the first to have been grown in Michigan?

   A.  Apple
   B.  Peach
   C.  Cherry

**ANSWER: B**

Peach trees were probably grown by William Burnett in the 1780s. He had a trading post at present-day St. Joseph, Michigan, on the St. Joseph River, one mile upstream from Lake Michigan.

What tunnel is the world's first underwater international tunnel?

   A.  Windsor Tunnel
   B.  Lincoln Tunnel
   C.  St. Clair Tunnel

**ANSWER: C**

The St. Clair Tunnel, connecting Sarnia, Canada, with Port Huron, Michigan, was opened in 1891 and is still one of the busiest international crossings in the world.

James Vernor, of Detroit, made a name for himself as the inventor of Vernor's ginger ale. However, that was not his first claim to fame.

What was James Vernor first known for?

   A.  Paving Vernor Avenue in Detroit
   B.  Being the first registered pharmacist
   C.  Hitting the first Tiger Stadium home run

**ANSWER: B**

Not only was James Vernor the inventor of Vernor's soda pop but also he was Michigan's first registered pharmacist. His pharmacist license was number 00001.

Many religious denominations are represented in Michigan.

**What**

What religious denomination had its first location in the United States in Michigan?

A. Muslim
B. Catholic
C. Methodist

**ANSWER: A, C**
The first mosque in the United States was established in Highland Park, Michigan, in 1919. The Society of Methodists built its first permanent building in River Rouge, Michigan, in 1818. By the way, St. Anne Parish in Detroit was built in 1701 and is the second-oldest Catholic parish in the country.

Since its founding in 1701, the city of Detroit has been home to three forts. Of these, only one still stands.
What fort in Detroit still stands in the city?

A. Fort Pontchartrain
B. Fort Wayne
C. Fort Shelby

**ANSWER: B**
Fort Wayne was completed in 1847 and was the last great fortress built in Detroit and the only one that still exists.
Fort Pontchartrain was the first, built by the French in 1701, marking the birth of the city, and Fort Shelby, originally Fort Lernoult, was built in 1779 by the British.

Of the five Great Lakes, Superior, Michigan, Huron, Erie, and Ontario, only one is entirely inside the borders of the United States.
What Great Lake is entirely inside the United States?

A. Lake Michigan
B. Lake Erie
C. Lake Huron

**ANSWER: A**
Of the five great lakes, only Lake Michigan is entirely inside the borders of the United States. It is bordered by the states of Michigan, Illinois, Indiana, and Wisconsin.

There are many lakes in the Great Lakes State. Michigan is known for lakes big and small. Michigan's largest non–Great Lakes lake is Houghton Lake in Roscommon County.

What is Michigan's second-largest lake, after Houghton Lake?

    A.  Torch Lake

    B.  Lake Charlevoix

    C.  Higgins Lake

**ANSWER: A**
Torch Lake in Antrim County is Michigan's second-largest non–Great Lakes lake, at more than 18,500 acres. Number three is Burt Lake in Cheboygan County, at 18,144 acres.

Douglas Houghton was a very accomplished man. He was Michigan's first geologist, surveying the state to find valuable minerals. He was also known for other jobs.

What other positions did Douglas Houghton hold, other than being Michigan's first geologist?

    A.  Physician

    B.  Mayor of Detroit

    C.  Insurance company executive

**ANSWER: A, B, C**
Douglas Houghton was quite a learned man and did all three jobs and more. He was a physician, served as mayor of Detroit, and was an executive of one of Michigan's first insurance companies. Dr. Houghton drowned, while surveying, at age 36 near Eagle Harbor in the Upper Peninsula in October 1845.

Famous sayings often come in the heat of battle, such as "Don't fire till you see the whites of their eyes." The commander of the First Michigan Engineers had a famous reply during the Civil War when asked to surrender by a Confederate general.

    What did he say?

    A.  "We don't surrender much."

    B.  "We have not yet begun to fight."

    C.  "Nuts!"

**What**

**ANSWER: A**

Colonel William Innes was commanding the Michigan First Engineers when his men were forced to protect an army position in Tennessee. When asked to surrender, he said, "We don't surrender much."

It was General McAuliffe who said "Nuts!" when the Nazis demanded his surrender at Bastogne during the Battle of the Bulge in WWII. Hero of the American Revolution John Paul Jones replied, "We have not yet begun to fight," when the British commander demanded that he surrender his fleet. None of them ended up surrendering.

Michigan is made up of two peninsulas, the Upper and the Lower. In the Upper Peninsula, there is a peninsula off of a peninsula.

What of these is a peninsula in Michigan's Upper Peninsula?

    A.  Keweenaw

    B.  Garden

    C.  Stonington

**ANSWER: A, B, C**

Both the Garden and Stonington peninsulas are in Delta County, jutting out into Lake Michigan. The Keweenaw Peninsula is almost as far north as you can go in Michigan and juts into Lake Superior.

The Motown sound is famous the world over, and many of those great Motown stars were born in the city of Detroit.

What famous Motown star was born in Detroit?

    A.  Aretha Franklin

    B.  Stevie Wonder

    C.  Jackie Wilson

**ANSWER: C**

Jackie Wilson, known as Mr. Entertainment, was the first real Motown star, and he was born in Detroit.

Aretha Franklin was born in Memphis, Tennessee, but grew up in Detroit, and Stevie Wonder was born in Saginaw, Michigan.

Governor George Romney was elected to office in 1962 and served until 1969, when he resigned to join the Nixon administration as secretary of HUD.

What did George Romney do before he became governor?

A. He was a state senator.
B. He headed a car company.
C. He was a college professor.

**ANSWER: B**
Before being elected governor, George Romney was head of American Motors from 1954 to 1962.

While states surrounding Michigan were settled in the early 1800s, the development of Michigan was much slower, not really getting started until almost 1830.

What held up the development of Michigan?

A. The black swamp
B. Indians
C. The Michigan/Ohio War

**ANSWER: A**
While Ohio, Illinois, Indiana, and Wisconsin were being settled in the early 1800s, Michigan's settlement was held up because of the big black swamp that cut across the region. In the 1820s, settlers began to drain the swamp, and settlement began to really move forward in the 1830s.

Often a court ruling has an effect on us all. That's why the cases that the court hears are such big news. In 1970, the Michigan Supreme Court made a major ruling.

What was that 1970 decision of the Michigan Supreme Court?

A. 18-year-olds could vote
B. Female attorneys could wear pantsuits in court
C. Toledo is in Michigan

**ANSWER: B**
Justice Thomas E. Brennan announced a ruling that it was acceptable for female attorneys to wear pantsuits in court—and thus another blow for fashion freedom.

What U.S. president signed the act that established the Michigan Territory?

A. John Adams
B. Thomas Jefferson
C. Andrew Jackson

**ANSWER: B**
President Thomas Jefferson signed the act establishing the Michigan Territory in January 1905. It was President Andrew Jackson who signed the act that made Michigan a state in 1836.

# "Where?"

## The great GREAT LAKES (*Where*) TRIVIA QUIZ

The Chevrolet Corvette is a classic sports car, the dream car of many around the world. The Corvette is also the premier model of Chevrolet.

Where was the first Corvette built?

A. Detroit, Michigan
B. Flint, Michigan
C. Bowling Green, Kentucky

ANSWER: B

The first Corvette was designed by the famous Harley Earl and named by Myron Scott after the fast ship of the same name. The first rolled off a Flint, Michigan, assembly line in June of 1953. That first Corvette had a sticker price of $3,250. The Vette is now built at a GM assembly plant in Bowling Green, Kentucky.

After Orville and Wilbur Wright invented the airplane, many others added their own touches to the technology of flying. In 1910, two brothers from Detroit landed a pontoon plane on water for the first time.

Where did that pontoon plane land?

A. Detroit River
B. Lake St. Clair
C. Ford Airport, Dearborn

ANSWER: A

The Alger brothers from Detroit successfully landed their pontoon plane on the Detroit River in 1910.

Americans love to visit the homes of famous people, from presidential homes, such as George Washington's Mount Vernon, to John Wayne's birthplace in Winterset, Iowa.

Where will we find the home of Orville and Wilbur Wright?

A. Kitty Hawk, North Carolina
B. Dayton, Ohio
C. Dearborn, Michigan

Where

**ANSWER: C**
The home of the Wright brothers is in Greenfield Village in Dearborn, Michigan, along with their bicycle shop. That is where Henry Ford put the buildings after he collected them, with many other historic buildings. The brothers were never married and lived in that home when it was on Hawthorne Street in Dayton, Ohio.

Prohibition began in Michigan in 1918, two years before the entire nation went dry. During that time, many people made their fortunes by smuggling alcohol into this country.

Where was the number one place to smuggle alcohol into the United States during Prohibition?

    A.  Sault Ste. Marie, Michigan
    B.  Buffalo, New York
    C.  Detroit, Michigan

**ANSWER: C**
Some estimates suggest that 75% of the liquor entering the United States during Prohibition came through what was called the Detroit-Windsor Funnel. In 1933, Michigan became the first state to ratify the Twenty-First Amendment, the one that ended Prohibition.

The American Red Cross has helped people from every corner of the globe deal with disaster for more than a century.

Where did the Red Cross provide its first relief effort?

    A.  Gettysburg
    B.  Michigan's Thumb
    C.  Cuba

**ANSWER: B**
The first Red Cross mission of mercy was to Michigan's Thumb region after the great fires of 1881. The fires burned more than a million acres and killed at least 281 people before they burned themselves out at the Lake Huron shore.

Frozen dinners, box mixes, takeout, and instant potatoes are all very common today. It wasn't that long ago that everything we ate was made from scratch, including cake.

Where was the first cake baking mix created?

A. Chelsea, Michigan
B. Ann Arbor, Michigan
C. Kalamazoo, Michigan

**ANSWER: A**

That first mix was called Jiffy, and it was made in Chelsea, Michigan, at the Chelsea Milling Company, in 1930. Jiffy Mix is the seventh-best-selling item at grocery stores today. Former race car driver Howdy Holmes is the third generation of his family to run the Chelsea Milling Company.

The Midwest loves its parties, and we have a lot of them, from the Cherry Festival and the Cool Jazz Festival to the Tulip Festival and the Potato Festival.

Where is the biggest festival in Michigan celebrated?

A. Traverse City, Cherry Festival
B. Holland, Tulip Festival
C. Munger, Potato Festival

**ANSWER: B**

Holland's Tulip Festival is not only Michigan's biggest festival but also one of the biggest festivals in the country, behind only Mardi Gras in New Orleans and the Tournament of Roses in Pasadena, California.

Most schools and community centers have a gymnasium, and most of them have a wood floor. They are so common that it is difficult to think of a time when there were no wood gym floors.

Where was the first wood gym floor built in the state of Michigan?

A. University of Michigan, Ann Arbor
B. Michigan Fairgrounds, Detroit
C. Eastern Michigan University, Ypsilanti

**Where**

The first wood gymnasium floor in Michigan was built at Eastern Michigan University, in Ypsilanti, in 1862, when the college was still known as Michigan State Normal School.

Community theater has been around for decades. Community theaters range in size from small groups that perform in borrowed spaces to large, permanent companies with facilities of their own. Many community theaters are nonprofit organizations with a large membership and even a full-time professional staff.
Where was the first community theater in the country started?

    A.  Newark, New Jersey
    B.  Chicago, Illinois
    C.  Calumet, Michigan

ANSWER: C
The first municipal theater in the country was founded in Calumet, Michigan, in the Upper Peninsula. It opened in May of 1911 with Sarah Bernhardt starring in *Camille*.

There are auto shows, flower shows, dog shows, coin shows, and fashion shows.
Where was the first aircraft show held?

    A.  Detroit, Michigan
    B.  Seattle, Washington
    C.  Oshkosh, Wisconsin

ANSWER: A
The first aircraft show in the country was held in 1928 at the Detroit Convention Center. The show attracted 63 planes from 40 manufacturers.

Music and musical instruments are big business. You will find a music shop in just about every town in the nation.
Where is the largest dealer of stringed instruments located?

    A.  New York, New York

**Where**

B.  Ann Arbor, Michigan

C.  Lansing, Michigan

**ANSWER: C**
The largest stringed instrument dealer in the world is in Lansing, Michigan. Elderly Instruments has more than 1,600 guitars in stock, from a Gibson Flying V that sells for thousands of dollars to a beginner's model for much less. The store was founded by a couple of University of Michigan graduates who discovered that Ann Arbor already had a music store.

There are some beautiful courthouses in Michigan. Many have been in use for more than a century.

Where is the Michigan courthouse that has been in use the longest?

A.  Lapeer

B.  Monroe

C.  Mackinac Island

**ANSWER: A**
The classic Lapeer County Courthouse, built in 1839, is still in use today. Even though a new court building was erected across the street from the old one, once every summer a judge in Lapeer County moves his court into the second floor of the old building to keep the record going.

The Detroit Pistons are now based at the Palace of Auburn Hills, Michigan.

Where was the Pistons' first home?

A.  Detroit, Michigan

B.  Fort Wayne, Indiana

C.  Kalamazoo, Michigan

**ANSWER: B**
The Pistons franchise was first located in Fort Wayne, Indiana. They have been the Detroit Pistons ever since they moved to Detroit in 1957. They have played in Pontiac and now play at Auburn Hills.

**Where**

Where was the first hospital in Michigan established?

A. Detroit
B. Saginaw
C. Grand Rapids

**ANSWER: A**
Michigan's first hospital was a log cabin built in Detroit in June of 1845. It was first called St. Vincent, and later the name was changed by the Sisters of Charity to St. Mary's Hospital.

Where is the oldest operating restaurant in Lapeer County, Michigan?

A. City of Lapeer
B. Imlay City
C. Village of Metamora

**ANSWER: C**
The oldest restaurant still in operation in Lapeer County is the White Horse Inn in Metamora. It was founded in 1872 as a stagecoach stop known as the Hoard House, named for its first owner.

When settlers first came to Michigan, they brought their bibles and families. When they got to their destinations, they usually built a church.
Where is the oldest church building in Genesee County?

A. Flint, Court Street Methodist
B. Grand Blanc, First Baptist Church
C. Mt. Morris, St. Mary's Catholic Church

**ANSWER: B**
The First Baptist Church, in Grand Blanc, is the oldest church building in Genesee County. It has been in active use since 1843.

Roads are the lifeline for any community.
Where was the first road surveyed in Michigan?

A. Detroit
B. Dexter
C. St. Ignace

**ANSWER: A**
The first road to be surveyed in Michigan was laid out in Detroit. It was called Pontiac Road; it ran between Detroit and Pontiac. You may be more familiar with Michigan's first road by what we call it today, Woodward Avenue.

We celebrate the Christmas holiday with lights, gifts, and goodwill to others.
Where was Michigan's first known Christmas celebrated?

A. Mackinac Island
B. Keweenaw Bay
C. Monroe

**ANSWER: B**
The first time Christmas was known to be celebrated was near Keweenaw Bay in the Upper Peninsula in 1660. Father René Menard wrote that he and "the Coureurs-de-bois celebrated with all the fervor possible under trying conditions of a primitive wilderness." The Coureurs-de-bois, or "woods runners" in French, were usually trappers.

Detroit is known as Hockeytown because of the Detroit Red Wings. Several Michigan colleges have won national championships in hockey, including the University of Michigan, Michigan State University, Northern Michigan University, and Lake Superior State University. Michigan loves its hockey.

Where was the first professional hockey team organized in the state of Michigan?

A. Detroit
B. Alpena
C. Houghton

**ANSWER: C**
The first pro hockey team in Michigan was organized in Houghton in 1903. A local mining company paid the players.

Michigan is the auto capital and auto pioneer of the world. Nameplates by the score came and went in the early days of the auto industry.

Where did the Briscoe, Imperial, Clark-Carter, Earl, and Cutting auto companies build their vehicles?

    A. Flint

    B. Jackson

    C. Highland Park

**ANSWER: B**
All of those old nameplates were built in Jackson.
Flint was the home of Buick, Chevrolet, and Dort, and Highland Park was where Henry Ford built his first factory in 1909.

The Michigan State Lottery was created in 1972 to raise extra revenue for education. Billions have been won and raised in the years since that first lottery ticket was sold.

Where is the first Michigan lottery ticket ever sold located now?

    A. Rob Jewell's attic

    B. Michigan History Museum

    C. No one knows.

**ANSWER: B**
The first Michigan lottery ticket is housed at the Michigan History Museum in Lansing. It was purchased on November 13, 1972, by Governor William Milliken at the state capital. The governor gave it to the Michigan Historical Commission.

Rob Jewell, a native of Boston, is an old friend of the author who is a community activist and a past president of the Rotary Club of Flint. He lives in Flint, serves on numerous boards, and is well known for saving everything in his extensive archives.

*Where* (margin)

Many Michigan communities are known for the products they produce: sugar beets in Sebewing, cherries in Traverse City, and beans in Caro.

Where is the sausage capital of Michigan?

A. Cedar
B. Hamtramck
C. Frankenmuth

**ANSWER: A**
Cedar, Michigan, claims to be the sausage capital of Michigan. Cedar is in Leelanau County, near Traverse City. That's where Pleva's Butcher Shop is located. Pleva invented cherry sausage and cherry burgers.

Michigan has a lot of lighthouses; it's got some pretty big lakes, too. Where is the oldest surviving lighthouse?

A. Port Huron
B. Muskegon
C. St. Ignace

**ANSWER: A**
Port Huron was also once known as Fort Gratiot. The Fort Gratiot Light was the first in Michigan, built in 1825. It was not well built, and after it collapsed in a storm, it was rebuilt in 1829 by Lucious Lyon, who later became one of Michigan's first U.S. senators. The light marks the entrance to the St. Clair River from Lake Huron.

Colleges offer many degrees, in biology, philosophy, literature, medicine, physics, economics—so many we can't name them all. A more recent course of university study is music.

Where was the first university degree in music awarded?

A. Adrian College
B. University of Michigan
C. Harvard

"Thar's gold in them hills." Those are words you expect to hear in California, but they have been heard in Michigan, too. There are gold mines in the Upper Peninsula; the Ropes Mine is near Marquette. In 1911, the Michigan Geological Survey reported that there was gold in Lower Michigan as well.

Where was gold found in 1911?

A. Durand
B. Kingston
C. Birmingham

An apple a day is good for your health. There have been some very big apples grown. Until 2005, the *Guinness Book of World Records* said the largest apple ever picked from a tree was grown in Michigan.

Where was that world-record apple grown?

A. Traverse City
B. Caro
C. Goodrich

The Civil War is considered the United States' great catastrophe. Thousands of Americans died in the conflict between the states. Michigan lost many in the war, and local communities dedicated more than 400 monuments to Civil War veterans.

Where was the first Civil War monument in Michigan?

A. Tipton
B. Flint
C. Detroit

ANSWER: A

The first Civil War monument in Michigan—and one of the first in the country—was dedicated on July 4, 1866, in the Franklin Township Cemetery in Lenawee County. The community later became Tipton. It is inscribed with the names of the 33 soldiers who lost their lives in the conflict. The inscription says it's a "memorial to the brave and patriotic men who represented them in battle and gave their lives in defense of the UNITY of our common country."

Ernest Hemmingway was a writer and journalist. He received the Pulitzer Prize in 1953 for *The Old Man and the Sea* and the Nobel Prize in Literature in 1954. Among his other works are *The Sun Also Rises*, *A Farewell to Arms*, and *For Whom the Bell Tolls*. As a young man, Hemmingway spent his summers in Michigan.

Where did Ernest Hemmingway spend his summers in Michigan?

A. Walloon Lake
B. Long Lake
C. Torch Lake

ANSWER: A

Hemmingway's family summer home, called Windermere, was at Walloon Lake. The lake is in Charlevoix and Emmet counties in northern Michigan. The Hemmingway home is on the north shore of the lake and is still owned by the Hemingway family.

Phones are essential equipment today. Not only do we have them in our homes and offices but also we carry them in our pocket.

**Where**

In the years before cell phones, a line had to be strung to have phone service.

Where was the first phone line in the state of Michigan?

A. Detroit
B. Lansing
C. Ontonagon

**ANSWER: C**

The first phone lines in Michigan were strung in 1876 by mine companies in Ontonagon in the Upper Peninsula. In March of 1877, Alexander Graham Bell's telephone made its debut in Detroit.

The lumber industry in Michigan has produced the wood that built great cities. Michigan's iron and copper have built the products that make the nation go. Michigan is also a leader in cement production.

Where is the world's largest cement plant?

A. Alpena
B. Muskegon
C. Rogers City

**ANSWER: A**

Alpena is the home of the world's largest cement plant. The Alpena Cement Plant has been producing materials for the construction industry since Huron Portland Cement Company was established in 1907 in Detroit. While it was established in Detroit, it operated in Alpena. The company has changed its name several times and is now part of the Lafarge Corporation.

Heavyweight boxing, sometimes called the "sweet science," has been popular since ancient times. The modern version includes champions in many weight classes. The "heavyweights" are at the top of the sport.

Where did the first heavyweight boxing championship bout in Michigan take place?

A. Saginaw
B. Adrian
C. Detroit

132

**ANSWER: C**
The first heavyweight title fight in Michigan took place in Detroit in 1900. At 250 pounds, Ohio farm boy James Jefferies defeated 180-pound John Finnegan in the first round.

Battles make history and reputations. There have been military battles in Michigan; the Battle of the River Raisin is one.

Where is the city in Michigan that was named in memory of a famous battle?

    A.  Buena Vista

    B.  Oscoda

    C.  Ishpeming

**ANSWER: A**
Buena Vista, in Saginaw County, was named in honor of General Zackary Taylor's victory during the Mexican War over General Santa Ana at a village called Buena Vista. The Battle of Buena Vista, also called the Battle of Angostura, took place in February of 1847._

There is one city in the country that can see the sun rise on one of the Great Lakes and set on another.

Where is the city that sees the sunrise on one lake and the sunset on another?

    A.  Milwaukee, Wisconsin

    B.  Mackinaw City, Michigan

    C.  Toledo, Ohio

**ANSWER: B**
Mackinaw City, at the tip of Michigan's Mitt, sees the sun rise on Lake Huron and sees it set on Lake Michigan.

Where was the only kingdom ever declared in the United States?

    A.  Beaver Island, Michigan

    B.  Kingston, Michigan

    C.  Empire, Michigan

**Where**

Where

**ANSWER: A**

In 1850, James Jesse Strang, who called himself "King Strang," brought 2,000 of his Mormon followers to Beaver Island and took over. He ruled the island until 1856, when he was murdered by one of his followers, thus bringing down his Beaver Island kingdom.

The Great Lakes states are winter sport destinations. Michigan is known as "the Winter Wonderland." A century-old industry has grown up around skiing.

Where was the National Ski Association formed?

    A. Traverse City, Michigan

    B. Ishpeming, Michigan

    C. Appleton, Wisconsin

**ANSWER: B**

The National Ski Association was formed in Ishpeming, Michigan, in 1904, just a few years after the country's first ski association had been formed there. That ski association founded in 1901 became the Ishpeming Ski Club. Today, Ishpeming is home to the National Ski Hall of Fame and Museum.

Phones have been around since before the turn of the twentieth century. Today you can make a call almost anywhere in the world.

Where was the first international phone line in the world?

    A. Sault Ste. Marie, Michigan, and Sault Ste. Marie, Canada

    B. Detroit, Michigan, and Windsor, Canada

    C. Port Huron, Michigan, and Sarnia Ontario, Canada

**ANSWER: B**

The first international phone line was opened between Detroit and Windsor in 1880.

In most communities, one of the first things settlers built was a church. In Michigan, the first Catholic parish, Ste. Anne de Detroit, was founded in Detroit in 1701.

Where is the next-oldest existing church in the state of Michigan?

A. Adrian
B. Detroit
C. Mackinac Island

**ANSWER: C**

The second-oldest existing church in Michigan is the Old Mission Church, on Mackinac Island, built in 1829. The Raisin Valley Friends Church in Lenawee County is the third oldest, built in 1834.

There have been many political parties in the history of the United States, from the Whigs and Know-Nothings to the Democrats and Republicans. Many people know that the first meeting of the Republican Party took place in Michigan.

Where did the first meeting of the American Communist Party take place?

A. Jackson, Michigan
B. Bridgman, Michigan
C. Ann Arbor, Michigan

**ANSWER: B**

In August of 1922, the first convention of the American Communist Party took place at the Wulfskeel farm, near Bridgman on Lake Michigan.

Civilization has arrived on the frontier when a community has a church, school, and library.

Where was the first library in the state of Michigan?

A. Detroit
B. St. Ignace
C. Port Huron

**ANSWER: A**

Michigan's first library was founded in Detroit in 1817. The City Library of Detroit was incorporated after the sale of 90 shares of stock at $5 a share.

**Where**

Ship builders are located wherever there is water. They build speedboats, freighters, schooners, canoes, and wood-hulled and steel-hulled vessels.

Where was the first steel-hulled vessel built in the United States?

  A.  Milwaukee, Wisconsin
  B.  Wyandotte, Michigan
  C.  Chicago, Illinois

**ANSWER: B**
The tug *Sport* was built, with a steel hull, in Wyandotte in 1873. It plied the Great Lakes until it sank in a storm in 1920 off the coast of the Thumb, near Lexington, in 47 feet of water. It was found by sport divers in 1987 and is today one of the most popular dive spots on the Great Lakes.

The year 1968 was tumultuous, with riots, the war in Vietnam, the assassinations of Senator Bobby Kennedy and Reverend Martin Luther King Jr. In March of 1968, Dr. King gave what was to be his last speech in Michigan before he was assassinated in April.

Where did Reverend Martin Luther King Jr. give his last speech in Michigan?

  A.  Saginaw
  B.  Grosse Pointe
  C.  Lansing

**ANSWER: B**
On March 14, 1968, Dr. King spoke at Grosse Pointe High School to a mostly white audience. While most in the audience were very supportive, there were a few loud protesters. The protesters were there because he had just come out against the war in Vietnam, saying it was unwinnable.

The first schools were primary schools, where students learned letters and numbers. It wasn't until much later that high schools formed.

Where was the first high school in Michigan?

  A.  Kalamazoo

B. Detroit

C. Grand Rapids

**ANSWER: B**

The Detroit Board of Education spent $150 to open a high school in 1844. No girls were allowed, and it was open for only a short time.

Michigan has been the site of a number of military battles, from the French and Indian War and the Revolutionary War to the War of 1812.

Where did the greatest battle ever fought on Michigan soil take place?

A. Monroe County

B. Mackinac Island

C. Near Detroit

**ANSWER: A**

The Battle of the River Raisin took place in Monroe County in January 1813, during the War of 1812. Two hundred Americans were killed, and more than 600 were taken prisoner. Those killed had surrendered and were mostly wounded. They were slaughtered by the British and their Native American companions. "Remember the River Raisin" became the battle cry during the War of 1812.

Michigan is a winter sport paradise, from skiing and skating to sledding, snowmobiling, and ice fishing. We know that the National Ski Hall of Fame is in Ishpeming, Michigan.

Where was the world-record ski jump set in 1996?

A. Ironwood, Michigan, Pine Mountain

B. Aspen, Colorado

C. Holly, Mount Holly

**ANSWER: A**

The record ski jump set in 1996 was 459 feet and was set at Pine Mountain in Ironwood, Michigan. Pine Mountain ski jump was built in 1938 by WPA workers. The first person to go down the jump was a WPA worker who went down on a shovel and broke an arm and both legs. The first successful jump was made by William Maki.

137

Rowing is a longtime sport. It is a varsity sport at many universities and is an Olympic sport as well.
Where was the first boat club in the country?

    A. Ann Arbor, Michigan
    B. Chicago, Illinois
    C. Detroit, Michigan

**ANSWER: C**
The oldest boat club in America is the Detroit Boat Club, founded in February 1839. It is the oldest sport rowing club in the United States. It is also the oldest continuously operating rowing club in the world.

When you were a kid, you probably wanted a Daisy air rifle, just like Ralphie in the movie *A Christmas Story* (though he wanted Red Ryder gun).
Where was the Daisy air rifle first manufactured?

    A. Rogers, Arkansas
    B. Cass City, Michigan
    C. Plymouth, Michigan

**ANSWER: C**
Daisy air rifles got their start in 1882 at the Plymouth Iron Windmill Company. By the late 1880s, the windmill business was fading, and the company began to look for a new product. In 1886, Plymouth inventor Clarence Hamilton suggested a gizmo that looked like a gun that could fire a lead ball using compressed air. When the company president, a man named Lewis Cass Hough, tried it out, he said, "Boy, that's a daisy!" The name stuck. In 1895, the company changed its name to Daisy Manufacturing Company Inc. In 1958, the company moved to Rogers, Arkansas.

He was baseball's iron man. Before his record was broken by Cal Ripken Jr., Lou Gehrig set the record at 2,130 games without a break. His streak ended in 1939, when he asked to be taken out of the lineup. He told his manager that he didn't have the energy to play that day, and he never played again. Less than a year later, he would be dead, killed by amyotrophic lateral sclerosis, now known as Lou Gehrig's Disease.

*Where*

Where did New York Yankees star Lou Gehrig play to end his streak of 2,130 games?

A.  Briggs Stadium, Detroit
B.  Yankee Stadium, New York
C.  Fenway Park, Boston

ANSWER: A

On May 2, 1939, Gehrig asked to be taken out of the game as New York prepared to play the Tigers at Briggs (later Tiger) Stadium.

We've often seen the Goodyear blimp at sporting events. An airship, or dirigible, is a lighter-than-air aircraft kept aloft by hot air or hydrogen. The use of these aircrafts decreased due to a series of high-profile accidents, including the 1937 burning of the hydrogen-filled Hindenburg near Lakehurst, New Jersey.

Where was the first all-metal dirigible constructed?

A.  Saginaw, Michigan
B.  Detroit, Michigan
C.  Flint, Michigan

ANSWER: B

The *ZMC-2*, America's first all-metal dirigible airship, was built in Detroit and first landed at Grosse Ile Airport in 1929. The big metal ship was piloted by Captain William C. Kepner, one of the country's leading balloonists. The ship remained aloft for 49 minutes.

The first national park is Yellowstone National Park, established by Congress in 1872. It is mostly in Wyoming, but it does extend into Montana and Idaho. The park was the first of its kind in the world.

Where was America's second national park?

A.  Mackinac Island National Park
B.  Sequoia National Park
C.  Yosemite National Park

**ANSWER: A (THEN B AND C)**

In 1875, the federal government established Mackinac Island National Park as the second national park, after Yellowstone. When Fort Mackinac closed its military operations in 1895, the federal government gave the park to the state of Michigan as its first state park.

Sequoia National Park and Yosemite National Park, both in California, became national parks in 1890 and are now technically our nation's second-oldest national parks.

Night baseball has been around for decades. Owners find that they can sell more tickets to night games. Plus, they discovered that teams make more money if they play the games at night on television and radio.

Where was the first night game, played under the lights, played?

A. New York
B. Alma
C. Grand Rapids

**ANSWER: C**

In July of 1909, Grand Rapids took on Zanesville, in the Central Baseball League, in the first regularly scheduled night game under the lights. Grand Rapids won that game 11-10. The last major-league baseball field to add lights was Wrigley Field in Chicago, the home of the Chicago Cubs. After a long battle by baseball traditionalists, the lights were turned on on August 8, 1988. The Cubs owners, the Tribune Company, had suggested that the team might move to the suburbs. By the way, that game was rained out, so the first official game under the lights at Wrigley was on August 9. The Cubs beat the Mets.

# "When?"

## The great GREAT LAKES (*When*) TRIVIA QUIZ

Some say radio was invented to play music. Actually, it was invented to send and receive emergency messages. Still, music has been a radio staple for years.

When was a symphony heard on the radio for the first time?

A. 1922
B. 1939
C. 1956

**ANSWER: A**

In 1922, the Detroit Symphony Orchestra presented the first ever symphony concert on Michigan's first radio station, WWJI in Detroit. The station went on the air in August of 1920. It is believed to be the first station to broadcast a regular newscast, the first regularly scheduled religious broadcast, and the first play-by-play sports broadcast.

Earthquakes are not common in the Great Lakes states. But in Michigan, there is an occasional quake just to remind people that they can occur.

When was the first earthquake recorded in Michigan?

A. 1663
B. 1798
C. 1887

**ANSWER: A**

An earthquake shook an area of North America known as New France in February 1663. That quake was recorded by Catholic missionaries in reports called "Jesuit Relations."

Legend says the first Thanksgiving was celebrated by the Pilgrims in 1621 at the Plymouth Plantation. They didn't know that there had already been a Thanksgiving celebrated, at St. Augustine, Florida, in September of 1565 by the Spanish.

When was Thanksgiving first celebrated in Michigan?

A. 1824
B. 1837
C. 1863

When

**ANSWER: A**

Michigan's first official Thanksgiving was held in 1824 by the decree of Governor Lewis Cass. He was influenced by the many New Englanders who had come to the new territory. Thanksgiving became a presidential proclamation in 1863, and it became an official national holiday in 1941.

---

The prison at Jackson, Michigan, has been around for a long time. It was once the largest walled prison in the world, with more than 6,000 inmates.

When did Jackson Prison get its first prisoner?

    A.  1800

    B.  1839

    C.  1876

**ANSWER: B**

Opened in 1838, Jackson Prison received its first inmate in 1839. His name was John McIntire, from Wayne County, and he had been convicted of larceny. That year, 55 more prisoners joined him. The prison was renamed the State Prison of Southern Michigan in 1935. Beginning in 1988, the prison was carved up into several correctional facilities. The Southern Michigan Correctional Facility, which contained the heart of the 1926 prison structure, was finally closed in 2007.

---

Daylight saving time is an old idea that is being used today to save energy and to give more daylight for evening outdoor activities.

When did Michigan voters approve daylight saving time?

    A.  1968

    B.  1972

    C.  1976

**ANSWER: B**

Voters in Michigan approved daylight saving time in 1972. It now adds an extra hour of daylight from March through Novemeber.

---

When a railroad came through a town, it changed everything for the people. The railroad brought in products and allowed local industry and farmers to send their goods to market. Trains were first powered by horses, men, and oxen. Later, steam powered the growth of rails around the country.

When did a steam-operated locomotive in Michigan make its last regular run?

A. 1927
B. 1957
C. 1965

**ANSWER: C**
In 1965, the last steam-powered train in the state went from Durand to Detroit on its final regularly scheduled run.

Weather forecasts and maps have been a part of our lives for as long as most of us remember. We see them every night on our local TV newscasts, in papers, and on our computer screens.

When was the first weather map made for Michigan?

A. 1888
B. 1922
C. 1939

**ANSWER: A**
In December of 1888, after two years of operation, the Michigan Weather Service made a map of rainfall in the state. It disseminated the forecast by putting weather flags on trains and train stations.

A Frenchman named Marin le Bourgeoys is credited by some with making the first firearm with a flintlock mechanism in 1610. This was the beginning of the muzzleloaders. It was muzzleloaders that tamed the west, but by the 1930s, muzzleloading was almost truly history. A comeback began in 1933, when the National Muzzle Loading Rifle Association was born near Shelbyville, Indiana. Today, there are shooting contests and hunts for muzzleloading enthusiasts. In Michigan and many other states, there are special muzzleloading seasons.

When did Michigan's first muzzleloading season take place?

When

A.  1923
B.  1955
C.  1975

**ANSWER: C**
The first "official" muzzleloading deer-hunting season took place in 1975. It is a time when only the muzzleloaders are in the woods.

Michigan is the motor capital of the world. It began registering vehicles more than 100 years ago.

When did the Michigan secretary of state register the two-millionth vehicle in the state of Michigan?

A.  1938
B.  1954
C.  1964

**ANSWER: C**
In 1964, Michigan Secretary of State James Hare issued the two-millionth vehicle title to William Schmitz in Lansing.

Every 10 years, by law, a census must be taken in the United States. It counts the number of people, how many are married, what they do, how they live, and where they live.

When did the census find that more people lived in cities than on farms in Michigan?

A.  1920
B.  1940
C.  1960

**ANSWER: A**
In 1920, for the first time, the census found that more people lived in Michigan cities than on its farms. The urban population in the state grew from 47% in 1910 to 61% in 1920.

The Rose Bowl and the Tournament of Roses have been around for a very long time. The Rose Bowl is known as the grandfather of all bowl games.

When was the first Rose Bowl played in Pasadena, California?

A. 1902
B. 1912
C. 1922

**ANSWER: A**
The first bowl game, the Rose Bowl, was played in January of 1902. Fielding Yost's Michigan Wolverines demolished Stanford 49-0 in that game.

Lots of folks head off to Florida during Michigan's winter. Often called "snowbirds," they go where it's warm.

When did the first Detroit to Miami airplane flight take place?

A. 1929
B. 1939
C. 1949

**ANSWER: A**
William Brock and Edward Schlee completed the first Detroit to Miami flight in January 1929. It took 9 hours and 20 minutes.

The three major sports teams in Detroit are among the oldest sports franchises in the big leagues. The Lions, the Tigers, and the Red Wings have pulled people together to cheer for their heroes since the turn of the twentieth century. One year was an especially good one to be a Detroit sports fan; all the teams won it all.

When did the Tigers, Lions, and Red Wings all win championships?

A. 1935
B. 1955
C. 1968

When

**ANSWER: A**
In 1935, the Tigers won the World Series against the Chicago Cubs, the Red Wings won the Stanley Cup against the Toronto Maple Leafs, and the Lions won the NFL championship against the New York Giants.

The University of Michigan is Michigan's first college, founded in 1817. It took a number of years before women were allowed to attend.

When was the first woman accepted at the University of Michigan?

    A.  1825
    B.  1870
    C.  1917

**ANSWER: B**
In 1870, the University of Michigan registered Madeline Stockwell of Kalamazoo as its first coed. She graduated in 1872 with a Bachelor of Arts degree.

Definitions are important things, especially in law. What is grand theft? What's the difference between drunk driving and driving under the influence? It may seem a silly question, but what is death?

When did the state of Michigan first define death?

    A.  1841
    B.  1928
    C.  1975

**ANSWER: C**
In 1975, Governor William Milliken signed a law that for the first time defined death as "when there are no longer brain waves on an encephalograph."

Snowmobiles are big business in the Great Lakes states. In northern Michigan, trails are becoming more popular and have turned into revenue generators. Snowmobile treks can go hundreds of miles.

When was the first snowmobile permitted to ride across the Mackinac Bridge?

A. 1965
B. 1970
C. 1990

**ANSWER: B**
Thirteen members of an Upper Peninsula snowmobile club crossed the Mackinac Bridge in February 1970, after paying the toll.

There are lots of "cat people" in Michigan; they love their cats! Did you know that in 1929, a law was passed that made it legal to shoot cats in Michigan? That law was later repealed.

When did Michigan law change to make it illegal to shoot cats?

A. 1930
B. 1950
C. 1978

**ANSWER: C**
In 1978, St. Clair Elementary School students watched as Governor William Milliken signed the law inspired by their campaign to make it illegal to shoot cats.

High school basketball is big in Michigan. Thousands go to see games every season, and many more are able to hear and see the games on radio and TV.

When was the first high school basketball game broadcast on television?

A. 1967
B. 1977
C. 1987

When

Drivers are always on the lookout for local police with speed radars, especially if the drivers have a tendency to drive a little too fast. Today, those radars are standard equipment in most police cruisers. When was speed radar first used in Michigan?  •

A.  1948
B.  1958
C.  1968

In the 1940s, Michigan began to issue full-color trout stamps to anglers to prove that they had paid for the right to fish trout.
When was the last trout stamp issued?

A.  1970
B.  1990
C.  1998

Fishing is one of the most popular sports in the United States and in Michigan.
When were fishing licenses first required in the state of Michigan?

A.  1891
B.  1925
C.  1955

**ANSWER: B**

In 1925, the state senate passed a law that forced anyone who wanted to fish in Michigan to pay for a license.

Michigan's hunting and fishing activities are big business. They bring in tourists and revenue that supports conservation and parks activities. That's why game wardens are so important.

When did Michigan hire its first game warden?

    A.  1887
    B.  1923
    C.  1953

**ANSWER: A**

Michigan's and the nation's first Game Warden was hired in 1887. His name was William Alden Smith from Grand Rapids. William Alden Smith (1859–1932) reportedly was the first salaried state game warden in the nation, from 1887 to 1891. Later, Smith was a U.S. representative (1895–1907) and U.S. senator (1907–1919) from the state of Michigan.

Fireworks are dangerous. In Michigan, only licensed fireworks operators are allowed to use anything much more than a sparkler.

When did the Michigan legislature vote to prohibit most fireworks? When did the State Of Michigan put restrictions on who could set off fireworks?

    A.  1909
    B.  1929
    C.  1949

**ANSWER: B**

In 1929, the Michigan legislature voted to prohibit the use of most fireworks by the general public.

Age counts in many things. You can't be president of the United States until you are 36, and you can't vote until you are 18. Age also counts when you have to quit something.

When

When can a Michigan judge no longer be appointed or elected?

A.  After 10 years on the bench
B.  After age 70
C.  There is no limit at all.

**ANSWER: B**
At age 70, a judge in Michigan cannot be elected or appointed to office. He or she may finish a term they were elected to before their seventieth birthday.

Taxes! We pay them on everything: sales, roads, gas, and the ever-popular "income" tax.
When did Michigan first adopt an income tax?

A.  1863
B.  1917
C.  1968

**ANSWER: C**
It wasn't until 1968 that Michigan joined many other states by adopting an income tax.

Since it was built, the Renaissance Center has been the defining mark in the skyline of Detroit.
When was the Renaissance Center dedicated?

A.  1967
B.  1977
C.  1987

**ANSWER: B**
The Ren-Cen's famous towers were dedicated in April of 1977. The force behind its construction was Henry Ford the Second who thought its construction would be a boon after the Detroit riots of Henry Ford II was the mover behind the building of the "RenCen" in 1977. Ford's leadership in this project is somewhat ironic since the Renaissance Center today is the home of General Motors.

For many years, Michigan governors were elected to two-year terms. Today, they can serve two four-year terms and no more.

When did Michigan's constitution change the term of office for governors from two to four years? When was a Michigan Governor was elected to a four year term for the first time?

A. 1928
B. 1949
C. 1966

**ANSWER: C**

In 1966, Michigan's constitution changed the governor's term of office from two to four years. In the 1990s, term limit activists across the country called for term limits, saying that elected officials had lost touch with constituents. In Michigan, term limits passed as a ballot initiative in 1992. Governors are limited to two four-year terms and legislators to three two-year terms in the House and two four-year terms in the Senate. U.S. Representative John D. Dingell, an opponent of term limits who has been in office since 1955, said, "Term limits have cut the legs off of a lot of giants in the legislature. By term limits, we may have sentenced ourselves to be run by pygmies."

Detroit Metro Airport in Romulus, Michigan, near Detroit, is the largest airport in the state and one of the biggest in the country.

When did the first regular passenger flight take off from Detroit Metro?

A. 1938
B. 1954
C. 1964

**ANSWER: B**

In April 1954, a DC 6-B Great Lakes clipper took off from Detroit Metro, headed for London, England.

Motion pictures are big business in America. From films starring John Wayne and Tom Hanks to Spencer Tracy and Angelina Jolie, they are a part of American life.

*When*

When was the first motion picture thought to have been screened in Michigan?

A. 1905
B. 1916
C. 1922

**ANSWER: A**
The first motion picture said to be screened in Michigan was shown in Detroit in 1905. At that time, the center of the movie-making world was still in New York and New Jersey.

Wild turkeys have been hunted in Michigan for centuries, but for many years, there were not enough to have a real hunting season.

When did Michigan have its first "official" wild turkey–hunting season?

A. 1926
B. 1957
C. 1965

**ANSWER: C**
Four hundred hunters got a license in 1965 and chased about 600 turkeys in Allegan County in Michigan's first modern-day turkey hunt. During that first nine-day season, 82 turkeys were bagged.

Cities around the Great Lakes are ports of call for ocean-going vessels, but that wasn't always so.

When were ocean-going vessels first able to sail the Great Lakes?

A. 1890
B. 1942
C. 1969

**ANSWER: C**
In April of 1969, the opening of the St. Lawrence Seaway opened the Great Lakes to seagoing ships for the first time.

According to the Michigan Constitution, the governor can call a meeting of the legislature in a place "other than Lansing."

When can the governor call a meeting of the legislature outside of the state capital?

A. When he or she feels like it
B. When Lansing is too dangerous
C. Where there is 5 feet of snow or 5 inches of rain

**ANSWER: B**
According to the Michigan Constitution, the governor of the state can call a meeting of the legislature outside of Lansing if "Lansing becomes dangerous for any reason."

The Michigan State Police was founded in 1917 as a wartime constabulary and eventually evolved into the modern agency that it is today. The department's enlisted members are called troopers.

When were women first allowed to be Michigan State Police troopers?

A. 1957
B. 1967
C. 1977

**ANSWER: B**
The first two women Michigan State Police troopers were sworn in in 1967.

Martin Luther King Jr. Day is now a national holiday celebrated in May, in connection with the birthday of the martyred civil rights leader.

When was Martin Luther King Jr. Day first celebrated in Michigan?

A. 1974
B. 1983
C. 1990

When

When the telegraph lines were strung across America, it seemed a miracle to regular folks. It changed the world even more than today's computer technology.

When was the first telegraph line in Michigan completed?

A. 1833
B. 1847
C. 1898

**ANSWER: B**
Michigan's first telegraph line was strung along the Michigan Central Railroad tracks from Detroit to Ypsilanti in 1847. The first messages were about the price of wheat and news on the Mexican-American War.

It seems that the threat of recall has stopped political leaders from attempting to solve, or even discussing, difficult political issues. However, in the early years of the state and republic, recalls were very rare.

When was the first Michigan legislator in history recalled?

A. 1873
B. 1937
C. 1983

**ANSWER: C**
After 147 years, the first legislator to be recalled was State Senator Phil Mastin, a Democratic from Pontiac who was recalled in 1983. His recall stemmed from his support of a temporary income tax hike.

Meijer stores are based in Michigan and are family owned. The story goes that Sam Walton, of Wal-Mart fame, copied what the Meijer stores were doing to be successful.

When did the first Meijer store open?

A.  1907
B.  1948
C.  1973

ANSWER: A

In 1907, 23-year-old Hendrik Meijer, a factory worker, came to Holland, Michigan, from his native Netherlands. He opened a grocery store in Holland, the first store in the chain, which became Meijer Thrifty Acres.

There were many years that newspapers were not published on Sundays for religious reasons. Later, the Sunday paper became the most popular and best seller of the week. When was the first regular Sunday edition of a newspaper published in Michigan?

A.  1853
B.  1917
C.  1931

ANSWER: A

It was in 1853 that the *Detroit Free Press* first began to publish a Sunday edition.

Red gas cans are a common sight in our garages, and they are a great place to store fuel for lawnmowers and snowmobiles.

When did Michigan law first require gas to be sold in red cans?

A.  1907
B.  1927
C.  1957

ANSWER: A

In 1907, Michigan law required gas to be sold only in approved red cans.

The Michigan State Lottery is big business and has been giving people a chance to win cash jackpots for many years.

When did Michigan draw its first lottery winner?

When

A. 1968
B. 1972
C. 1976

**ANSWER: B**
Michigan's first lottery ticket numbers were drawn on November 23, 1972, at Detroit's Cobo Hall. The numbers were 130 and 544.

The Shrine Circus is a major fundraiser for the Shrine Charities of the Masonic Organization. The first Shrine Circus was held in Detroit.
When was the first Shrine Circus held?

A. 1887
B. 1906
C. 1946

**ANSWER: B**
The Shrine Circus was first performed in 1906. About 3,000 spectators saw the show. It was called "the Mystic Shriner's Yankee Circus in Egypt." Today it travels to 120 cities in the United States every year. The first Shrine Circus was held in Detroit, Michigan, for the Moslem Shrine Center. There is a state historical marker at the site.

Lighthouses have been a part of Great Lakes lore for almost two centuries. The first light on the lakes was put up at Port Huron, then called Fort Gratiot.
When was the first light to guide ships through the dangerous waters of the Straits of Mackinac established?

A. 1798
B. 1831
C. 1862

**ANSWER: B**
While there are many lights on the Straits of Mackinac, including White Shoal, Spectacle Reef, and the Round Island Light, the first light at the straits was actually a lightship that began service in 1831. The last of the Great Lakes lightships is now a museum ship at Port Huron, Michigan.

One of the nation's first planned communities was built in Flint, Michigan. The Civic Park area was built, along with many other homes throughout the city, to house workers who came to town to work at the Buick and Chevrolet plants.
When did construction of the Civic Park area begin?

    A.  1892
    B.  1919
    C.  1933

**ANSWER: B**
In March of 1919, the Modern Housing Corporation, owned by General Motors, began to build 1,000 homes on what had been the old Stockdale and Durant farms. Five sawmills and a railroad were built, and more than 4,600 workers worked 24 hours a day to build the community.

Got a map in your glove box? Road maps have always been very important to travelers and sometimes hard to find.
When was the first road map of Michigan published?

    A.  1745
    B.  1800
    C.  1826

**ANSWER: C**
In 1826, engineers laying out the road from Detroit to Chicago sent their information to Washington, D.C., where the first Michigan road map was published.

Pro football's top showcase is the Super Bowl. That event has happened in Michigan twice, with the last one being at Ford Field in 2006.
When was the first Super Bowl played in Michigan?

    A.  1968
    B.  1977
    C.  1982

**When**

**ANSWER: C**

The first Super Bowl played in Michigan, Super Bowl 16, was actually played in Pontiac, at the Silverdome, in 1982. More than 81,000 fans in the stadium and 105 million at home watched as the San Francisco 49ers beat the Cincinnati Bengals 26-21. Super Bowl 40 was played at Ford Field in 2006 as Pittsburgh beat Seattle 21-10 for the title.

The first houses built by Europeans in Michigan were very simple buildings, with few or no windows. Even when a fancy house was built, there still weren't many windows, and they were small because the glass had to be imported.

When was the first glass manufactured in Michigan?

A. 1763
B. 1835
C. 1957

**ANSWER: B**

Dr. Ebenezer Hall arrived in Mount Clemons, Michigan, in 1835 with workers, bricks, and more to establish the Mount Clemens Glass Works, the first window maker in Michigan.

Michigan has been under the flags of four nations and has been a territory, a frontier, an outpost, and a state. Through it all, it has had judges. For most of those years, a judge did not have to be an attorney.

When did Michigan law require that a judge also had to be an attorney?

A. 1803
B. 1942
C. 1969

**ANSWER: C**

It wasn't until 1969 that district judges, who were required to be attorneys, replaced all municipal judges and justices of the peace.

# The Who, What, Where, When, Why and How of Michigan

The University of Michigan has been fielding a football team for more than a century. It is one of the most storied football programs in college sports.

When did the Michigan Wolverines play for the first time in an enclosed stadium?

    A.  1975
    B.  1982
    C.  1989

**ANSWER: B**
Coach Bo Schembechler's Wolverines trounced UCLA 33-14 in the Blue Bonnet Bowl in the Houston Astrodome in 1982.

Michigan's territorial capital and first state capital were located in Detroit. Detroiters wanted to keep the capital, but the legislature voted to move it to the wilderness of Lansing.

When did Michigan's state capital move to Lansing?

    A.  1837
    B.  1847
    C.  1858

**ANSWER: B**
On Christmas Day 1847, the state's records were secretly taken to the banks of the Grand River in what is now Lansing. They had to sneak out of Detroit because the locals wanted the capital to remain in Detroit.

In Michigan, the age when people can legally drink alcohol has been 21 for many years, except for a seven-year period when the age was 18.

When did the Michigan law change back the age to legally consume alcohol from 18 to 21?

    A.  1970
    B.  1976
    C.  1978

**ANSWER: C**
In December of 1978, the legal age to drink in Michigan returned to 21 after Michigan voters changed the law in a referendum.

Some simple history dates: The United States (colonies) declared independence in 1776. The Revolution ended in 1783.
When did the first U.S. flag fly over Michigan?

    A.  1783
    B.  1796
    C.  1807

**ANSWER: B**
On July 11, 1796, 13 years after the victory over the British for American independence, Captain Moses Porter brought the flag to Detroit and took possession of the Michigan Territory. In September, the flag finally flew over Fort Mackinac, on Mackinac Island.

It's been called one of the best and most familiar college fight songs in history, the University of Michigan's "Hail to the Victors."
When was "Hail to the Victors" written?

    A.  1895
    B.  1915
    C.  1947

**ANSWER: A**
The fight song, whose actual title is "The Victors," was written in 1895 by Louis Elbel, a student at U of M, following a victory over the University of Chicago football team. John Philip Sousa said it was "the greatest college fight song ever written."

Al Kaline is one of the greatest ballplayers ever to grace a Detroit baseball team. He was the twelfth player to collect more than 3,000 hits and was elected to the National Baseball Hall of Fame in his first year of eligibility.
When did Hall of Famer Al Kaline retire as a player?

    A.  1969

B. 1974
C. 1984

**ANSWER: B**

Tiger great Al Kaline retired after the 1974 season. He won a batting title at the age of 20, won 10 Gold Gloves, was a member of the 1968 World Series Champion Detroit Tigers, and had 3,007 hits and 399 home runs. In 1980, he became the tenth player elected to the Hall of Fame the first year he was eligible.

In the years before the Mackinac Bridge connected Michigan's Upper and Lower peninsulas, the only way to get a car to the Upper Peninsula was to go through Wisconsin or take a car ferry across the straits from Mackinaw City to St. Ignace.

When did the car ferry first cross the Straits of Mackinac?

A. 1923
B. 1938
C. 1946

**ANSWER: A**

The Michigan Highway Department started car ferry service in 1923. In the ferry's 35 years of existence, it used eight ferries and transported more than 11 million cars and 30 million people. During peak periods, a driver might have to wait anywhere from 4 to 15 hours for a turn to cross.

Michigan has become one of the nation's top wine-producing states. The land, climate, and waters of western Michigan, along Lake Michigan, especially in the northwest and southwest sections of the state, are especially well adapted to growing grapes.

When did the first wine-making operation in Michigan open?

A. 1878
B. 1903
C. 1962

**ANSWER: B**

Michigan's first winery was opened in Lawton, near Kalamazoo, in 1903. Today, Michigan is among the top 10 producers of wine and is in the top five producers of grapes in the country.

**When**

One of the most controversial motor vehicle laws in the state of Michigan is the motorcycle helmet law. While it has undoubtedly saved thousands of lives and prevented grave injuries, many argue it is their right to go without a helmet while on a ride.

When did the motorcycle helmet law first go into effect?

    A. 1960
    B. 1969
    C. 1979

**ANSWER: B**
The Michigan law that required anyone riding a motorcycle to wear a helmet went into effect in 1969. An earlier law passed in 1967 had been declared unconstitutional.

If you've ever watched a good John Wayne western, you have seen a stagecoach robbery. Many believe all those legendary stagecoach robberies took place in the Wild West, but there were stagecoach robberies in Michigan as well.

When did the last stagecoach robbery take place in Michigan?

    A. 1863
    B. 1889
    C. 1913

**ANSWER: B**
The last known stagecoach robbery in Michigan took place in 1889 when Reimund Holzhey robbed a stagecoach near Lake Gogebic in the Upper Peninsula. He shot and killed one of the passengers but was caught and spent the rest of his life in prison.

Isle Royale National Park in Lake Superior is a rustic wilderness and one of the least visited national parks in the country. It is also Michigan's only national park.

When was Isle Royale National Park established?

    A. 1887
    B. 1946
    C. 1953

**ANSWER: B**
Isle Royale National Park was established by Congress in 1946. While Isle Royale is the only national park in Michigan, there are other sites associated with the National Park Service in Michigan.
Keweenaw National Historic Park, Calumet
Sleeping Bear Dunes National Lakeshore, Empire
Motor Cities National Heritage Area, Detroit
North Country Scenic Trail, seven states, from New York to North Dakota

Once there were so many that witnesses said they blackened the sky for hours. It seemed that there were so many passenger pigeons that you couldn't kill them all. But we did; passenger pigeons were hunted to extinction.

When did the last known passenger pigeon die?

A. 1836
B. 1892
C. 1914

**ANSWER: C**
A passenger pigeon named Martha, the last of its species, died in 1914 at the Cincinnati, Ohio, Zoo. The last passenger pigeon shot in a hunt is thought to have been taken in 1900 in Pike County, Ohio.

The U.S. Postal Service has been delivering mail for more than 200 years. Mail has been carried on horseback and by train, ship, pony express, truck, and men and women.

When was the first airmail delivered in Michigan?

A. 1920
B. 1926
C. 1953

**ANSWER: A**
A seaplane brought the first airmail delivery to Detroit on August 17, 1920. Regular airmail service began in 1926.

**When**

165

Friday night high school football in Michigan is a great tradition and is very popular.

When was the first high school football game played?

A. 1888
B. 1910
C. 1922

**ANSWER: A**

In 1888, Detroit High School played its first formal football game against a rugby team from Windsor, Ontario, Canada. They used football rules, and the rugby team won 12-6.

The state of Michigan was the first state in the union and among the first in the Western world to ban capital punishment. Michigan banned the death penalty in 1846.

When did the last execution take place in Michigan?

A. 1845
B. 1860
C. 1938

**ANSWER: C**

In 1938, Anthony Chebatoris was hanged at Milan Prison for killing someone while robbing a Midland bank. Because he robbed a bank, he was charged with a federal crime under federal law instead of state law, and that is why he was legally executed in Michigan.

I-75 is the main route north and south through Michigan. It also runs from Michigan to Florida.

When was I-75 completed from the Ohio border to the Upper Peninsula?

A. 1962
B. 1973
C. 1980

General Motors, born in Flint, with its home base in Detroit, has suffered some financial difficulties over the past few years. It seems to be coming around, but it has been a big fall for a corporation that was once the largest and most profitable in the world.

When did GM stock first appear on the New York Stock Exchange?

A. 1911
B. 1923
C. 1936

Among the great mysteries in Michigan and labor union history is the disappearance of Teamsters Union leader Jimmy Hoffa. The search continues for his body or some clue as to what happened to the former labor leader.

When did Jimmy Hoffa disappear?

A. 1970
B. 1975
C. 1980

Women in the United States were not always equal. In fact, there was a time when they could not own property in their own right. Women were not given the right to vote in the constitution.

**When**

When did women in Michigan get the right to vote?

A.  1867
B.  1918
C.  1920

**ANSWER: A**
Women taxpayers were given the right to vote in school elections in Michigan in 1867, but it wasn't until 1918 that a woman could vote for other offices in Michigan. It took even longer in other states—1920 to be exact—for women's suffrage to become universal by an act of Congress.

The Ford Model T changed the world. Henry Ford produced more than 15 million of them, starting in 1908.
When was the last Model T built?

A.  1910
B.  1920
C.  1927

**ANSWER: C**
The Ford Model T was built for 19 years, until 1927. The idea was that the Model T was a vehicle for the common man. Mr. Ford liked to say you could get a Model T in any color, as long as it was black. Ford did build six Model Ts to celebrate its centennial in 2003.

According to legend, the first Republican Party Convention was held in 1854, under the oaks, in Jackson, Michigan.
When was the first Republican governor in the United States elected?

A.  1854
B.  1876
C.  1919

**ANSWER: A**
In 1854, Kingsley S. Bingham, a farmer and former state representative, was elected Michigan's tenth governor and the nation's first Republican governor.

There are plenty of places to see a live concert in Michigan today, from Detroit's Orchestra Hall and Flint's Whiting to the Palace of Auburn Hills, the Midland Event Center, and Van Andel Arena in Grand Rapids.

When did the first formal concert take place in Michigan?

A. 1832
B. 1870
C. 1910

ANSWER: A

In June of 1832, Mr. Bliss, a Tyrolean singer, performed at the territorial capital in Detroit. A ticket cost 25 cents.

One of the great traditions of the Great Lakes is sailboat racing. Two of the biggest sailing events in the world are the Chicago to Mackinac race and the Port Huron to Mackinac race.

When did the first Port Huron to Mackinac race take place?

A. 1867
B. 1898
C. 1925

ANSWER: C

The first Port Huron to Mackinac boat race took place in 1925. Instituted by the Bayview Yacht Club in Detroit, the first race had 12 participating boats.

The granddaddy of Great Lakes boat races is the Chicago to Mackinac boat race. The first Chicago to Mackinac race took place in 1898, sponsored by the Chicago Yacht Club.

Today, Little League baseball is for both boys and girls. But that wasn't always so. Girls were not allowed to play with the boys for many years.

When did girls first get to play on a Little League baseball team?

A. 1963
B. 1973
C. 1983

**ANSWER: B**

In 1973, 12-year-old Carolyn King, who had beat out three boys to make the team, was allowed to play in the Little League in Ypsilanti, Michigan. At first, the National Little League Association suspended the Ypsilanti group, but they were soon to drop the boys-only policy, as mandated by the federal government.

The Free and Accepted Masons are one of the most well-known fraternal organizations in the world. Michigan citizens have been a part of the Masons for a very long time.

When did the Masons start their first lodge in Michigan?

    A. 1764
    B. 1836
    C. 1965

**ANSWER: A**

In 1764, the Masonic Organization of New York issued a charter for Michigan's first Masonic Lodge. Detroit Lodge of Masons Number 1 was the first Masonic Lodge west of the Alleghenies.

The city of Detroit is the oldest in Michigan and, since its founding in 1701, one of the oldest cities in the country. The Detroit Fire Department is also one of the oldest.

When did the Detroit Fire Department use horses to pull a fire rig on a regular run for the last time?

    A. 1922
    B. 1938
    C. 1946

**ANSWER: A**

In 1922, the Detroit Fire Department's last horse-drawn fire rig made a five-minute run through the city. In June 1805, a fire practically leveled Detroit. After that, an ordinance required every citizen to have a full water barrel and two buckets ready to fight a fire. Bucket brigades of men, women, and even children moved water from the river to the fire. It wasn't until 1860 that the city finally hired its first paid fire fighters.

Ste. Anne Catholic Church in Detroit was founded in 1701 by the first French settlers. Of course, they spoke French in their community and church.

When was the last Mass said in French in Detroit?

A. 1776
B. 1838
C. 1942

**ANSWER: C**

Mass was said in French as late as 1942. You might be surprised to learn that as late as the 1940s, there were people born in Detroit who grew up speaking French as their first language.

If you know about Michigan and Ohio history, you know there was a major controversy over the Toledo Strip. That strip, which had been marked off as Michigan territory, was claimed by Ohio. Ohio demanded Toledo in return for its vote on Michigan statehood in 1836. Ohio got it, and Michigan ended up with the Upper Peninsula. But the controversy continued.

When was the Michigan-Ohio border officially and finally settled?

A. 1836
B. 1870
C. 1915

**ANSWER: C**

It wasn't until 1915 that the border dispute between Michigan and Ohio was settled by Michigan Governor William Ferris and Ohio Governor Frank Willis.

Laws banning smoking in establishments and schools have become more and more popular around the country. Most workplaces no longer allow smoking, and many other places are banning smoking.

When did Michigan law first limit smoking in grocery stores and restaurants?

A. 1966
B. 1971
C. 1977

**ANSWER: C**
The Michigan legislature passed a law that banned smoking in grocery stores and required restaurants seating more than 50 to provide nonsmoking areas in 1977.

Traffic laws are constantly being studied to find ways to make traffic flow better.

When did the law making it legal to make a right turn after a stop on a red light take effect in Michigan?

A. 1960
B. 1970
C. 1976

**ANSWER: C**
The right turn on red law took effect in Michigan in March of 1976, and it does make traffic move more efficiently.

Education is a top priority for citizens in the Great Lakes region. Schools were always a topic of interest as the states, including Michigan, began to develop.

When did Michigan government first deal with the idea of schools?

A. 1787, Northwest Ordinance
B. 1837, constitution
C. 1960, constitutional convention

**ANSWER: A**
Education was first addressed in the Northwest Ordinance of 1787. That law governed the Northwest Territory and laid out a map to statehood for Michigan, Illinois, Ohio, and Wisconsin. The ordinance was also the first U.S. law that banned slavery.

Michigan historical markers mark people, places, buildings, and events that have historic significance.

When did the first Michigan historical marker include an inscription in Braille?

A. 1960
B. 1986
C. 1998

**ANSWER: B**
In September of 1986, a Michigan historical marker was dedicated at the Michigan School for the Blind in Lansing. Stevie Wonder, a former student at the school, was there to mark the occasion.

These days, we seem to get several kinds of phone books, from the phone companies, from advertisers, from organizations. There are also many kinds of yellow books.

When was the first real phone book published in Michigan?

A. 1878
B. 1910
C. 1926

**ANSWER: A**
The first phone book in Michigan was published in Detroit in 1878.

To drive a motor vehicle in Michigan, you must have and carry a valid driver's license.

When did the state law that required drivers to carry a license go into effect?

A. 1910
B. 1919
C. 1925

**ANSWER: B**
In 1919, the law in Michigan began to require a driver to carry a license. About 250,000 residents applied for a license, but they did not have to pass a test.

**When**

It wasn't long after the Wright brothers flew their contraption at Kitty Hawk, North Carolina, that there were planes flying in the skies over Michigan.

When did a jet plane first make its appearance in the skies over Michigan?

    A.  1946
    B.  1953
    C.  1961

**ANSWER: A**
The first jet to fly over Michigan was a P-80 that flew from Selfridge Air Force Base in Mt. Clemons during a Civil Air Patrol show in 1946.

Many consider the Mackinac Bridge one of the great engineering marvels of the world. People dreamed of connecting the Upper and Lower peninsulas for centuries.

When did a Michigan governor for the first time speak publicly of building a bridge between the peninsulas?

    A.  1867
    B.  1912
    C.  1930

**ANSWER: C**
The first governor to talk out loud about a bridge over the Straits of Mackinac was Governor Fred Green in 1930. His idea was to build several bridges from island to island to get across the straits. The bridge was opened in 1957.

For its first decades of existence, the Michigan State Police was an all-white men's club.

When was the first African American sworn in as a Michigan State Police trooper?

    A.  1957
    B.  1967
    C.  1977

**ANSWER: B**
It wasn't until 1967 that the first African American police officer was sworn in as a Michigan State Police trooper. He was Jack Hall, a former Benton Township police officer.

Since coming to Detroit, the Detroit Lions have played at four stadiums. The first was the University of Detroit football stadium; then came Tiger Stadium, the Pontiac Silverdome, and Ford Field.

When did the Lions play their first game at the Pontiac Silverdome?

    A. 1969
    B. 1975
    C. 1980

**ANSWER: B**
The Lions played their first game at the Pontiac Silverdome on August 23, 1975, and they won! They beat the Kansas City Chiefs 27-24.
    UD Stadium: 1934–1937, 1940
    Detroit Tiger (Briggs) Stadium: 1938–1939, 1941–1974
    Pontiac Silverdome: 1975–2001
    Ford Field: 2002–present

**When**

Although newspapers are changing and there are few dailies left in Michigan, they have a long history in the state.

When was the first newspaper published in Michigan?

    A. 1797
    B. 1809
    C. 1836

**ANSWER: B**
Michigan's first paper was published in 1809. It was called the *Michigan Essay* or *Impartial Observer*. It was published only once. The *Detroit Free Press*, thought of as Michigan's oldest existing newspaper, was first published in 1831.

Motoring across the state is a breeze these days because of the freeway system. Those highways make traveling much easier all over the country.

When did Michigan's first freeway open?

A. 1942
B. 1952
C. 1960

**ANSWER: A**

Michigan's first freeway opened in 1942. Like many things, it was a war effort. That first Michigan freeway was along US 12 and went from Detroit to the Ford Willow Run plant, then manufacturing bombers for WWII.

Colleges and universities were created to educate men. Women generally were educated at convent schools and at all-women schools. Even after women were accepted into universities, such as the University of Michigan, they were not able to take part in all activities, such as the famous University of Michigan marching band.

When were women finally allowed to join the University of Michigan marching band?

A. 1944
B. 1965
C. 1972

**ANSWER: C**

It wasn't until 1972 that women were allowed to march in the University of Michigan marching band. Two years later, pom-pom girls were allowed to perform in the Big House for the first time.

Today, we have phones everywhere. We can make a call from literally anywhere.

When did the first air-to-ground phone calls take place?

A. 1947
B. 1957
C. 1967

**ANSWER: B**

In 1957, the first air phone service was set up on 29 planes on the Detroit to Chicago run.

Do you remember the "safety patrol" at your school? These were the kids who wore the safety patrol belts and helped younger kids get across the street before and after school.

When were the first safety patrols set up?

A. 1910
B. 1920
C. 1957

**ANSWER: B**

The first safety patrols were set up in Detroit in 1920 by the American Automobile Association (AAA). Today, there are upward of a half-million young people who are members of safety patrols at their schools, and millions, including the author, were patrol guards while they were in school.

We see those red, amber, and green traffic lights everywhere. They help maintain a safe traffic flow.

When was the first red light signal installed?

A. 1910
B. 1920
C. 1930

**ANSWER: B**

In 1920, a traffic light was installed at Woodward Avenue in Detroit. It was invented by Detroit Police Lieutenant William Potts. Today that light is on display at the Henry Ford Museum in Dearborn.

Michigan changed the way auto insurance worked when it decided that insurance should cover the insured vehicle without determining who is at fault in an accident; it's called "no-fault" insurance.

When did Michigan's no-fault insurance law go into effect?

A. 1973
B. 1980

**When**

177

C. 1983

**ANSWER: A**
Michigan's no-fault insurance law went into effect in 1973.

Teachers in Michigan have several professional organizations and unions they can be associated with. The Michigan Education Association is the largest and most powerful teachers union in the state.
When was the Michigan Education Association formed?

A. 1852
B. 1907
C. 1937

**ANSWER: A**
In 1852, the Michigan State Teachers Association was organized. That was back when most teachers taught in a one-room schoolhouse. It became the MEA in 1926.

For many years, the Michigan standards for hot dogs and lunch meat were higher than federal standards. But some national meat processors filed a lawsuit to get those Michigan standards overturned. A federal appeals court agreed, saying it was illegal for a state to have standards higher than national standards require.
When did the federal court rule that lower federal meat standards would replace Michigan standards?

A. 1960
B. 1972
C. 1980

**ANSWER: B**
In 1972, the stronger Michigan standards for meat products were dropped by court order. However, some Michigan packers, such as Koegel Meats based in Flint, Michigan, kept the higher standards and built their advertising campaigns around making their products "up to Michigan standards."

When civilization reached the frontier, the first thing residents did was build a church, a grist mill, a school, and a jail.

When was the oldest jail house in Michigan, still in use, built?

A. 1886
B. 1906
C. 1916

ANSWER: A

The oldest jail, still in use, in the state of Michigan is the Keweenaw County Jail in the Upper Peninsula. It was built in 1886.

Bowling is a growing sport. There are now high school teams, and more are being added all the time. Bowling leagues are very popular, and the pro-bowling circuit is also doing very well.

When did a professional bowler make more than $100,000 in winnings for the first time?

A. 1965
B. 1975
C. 1985

ANSWER: B

In 1975, Earl Anthony won $8,000 at the Buz Fazuio Open in Battle Creek. That put him over the $100,000 mark that year.

Every year in the state of Michigan, vehicle owners must get a new license tag. These days, the due date for new tags is the owner's birthday, but that wasn't always so. There was a time when all license tags were due on the same day.

When did the law take effect that changed the deadline for purchasing license plates to the owner's birthday?

A. 1955
B. 1979
C. 1980

When

Three Michigan cities boast a bridge crossing to Canada: Detroit's Ambassador Bridge, Port Huron's Blue Water Bridge, and Sault Ste. Marie's International Bridge.
When did the International Bridge at the Soo open?

A.  1925
B.  1962
C.  1972

**ANSWER: B**
The International Bridge in Sault Ste. Marie was opened in 1962. The Ambassador Bridge in Detroit opened in 1929, and the first Blue Water Bridge, in Port Huron, opened in 1938. The second span opened in 1997.

Occasionally, you can still make out an old advertisement on the side of a rural barn. Barn advertising was very popular as early as the 1800s. But in Michigan, those big ads on the sides of barns, such as the Chew Mail Pouch Tobacco graphics, were banned.
When did barn advertising in Michigan become illegal?

A.  1960
B.  1968
C.  1974

**ANSWER: C**
In 1974, the state of Michigan banned barn advertising. The state painted over 47 barns.

Mackinac Island is famous all over the world as an island with no motor traffic. In 1949, all motor traffic was banned. Later, the island's leaders decided that snowmobiles would be OK.
When did the residents of Mackinac Island decide to allow snowmobiles on the island?

A. 1952
B. 1962
C. 1972

**ANSWER: C**
Operating a snowmobile on Mackinac Island became legal in 1972.

Fans of high school football all know about the amazing season Saginaw Arthur Hill High School had. It is the only team in Michigan history to go undefeated and unscored on for an entire season.

When did Saginaw Arthur Hill High go undefeated and unscored on?

A. 1960
B. 1973
C. 1980

**ANSWER: B**
The Lumberjacks of Saginaw Arthur Hill High outscored their opponents 443-0 and won nine games in 1973.

Today, talk about genetic testing and DNA is common. These topics have major implications for the future. The nation's first "heredity" clinic was built in Michigan to look into these issues.

When was the nation's first heredity clinic opened?

A. 1941
B. 1971
C. 1991

**ANSWER: A**
In 1941, the University of Michigan established the nation's first heredity clinic in Ann Arbor. The clinic collects data on human heredity and offers family counseling.

**When**

The Michigan high school football playoffs are quite popular around the state. Before the playoffs, mythical state champions were selected.
When did the first Michigan high school football playoff take place?

A.  1962
B.  1968
C.  1975

**ANSWER: C**
In 1975, the Michigan High School Athletic Association crowned playoff champions for the first time.
Class A: Livonia Franklin
Class B: Dearborn Devine Child
Class C: Ishpeming
Class D: Crystal Falls

Michigan has been at the forefront of aviation since just after the Wright brothers' first flight at Kitty Hawk, North Carolina. Detroit had one of the first aero clubs in the country.
When was the Detroit Aero Club founded?

A.  1909
B.  1920
C.  1935

**ANSWER: A**
In 1909, 75 prominent Detroiters met at the Ponchartrain Hotel with special guests Orville and Wilbur Wright to organize Michigan's first aero club. After the meeting, they conducted Detroit's first airport survey by car.

The Detroit Tigers are more than 100 years old. Baseball has been played in Detroit even before the Tigers came to town.
When did professional baseball first get organized in Detroit?

A.  1880
B.  1900
C.  1910

**ANSWER: A**

The Detroit Baseball Company, the forerunner of the Detroit Tigers, was organized in 1880 and played in the National League until 1888. In 1894, the Detroit Tigers Baseball Club organized as one of the American League's eight charter franchises.

We pay taxes on everything, from cable service and restaurant meals to home purchases and income, but in Michigan we do not pay taxes on food and prescription drugs.

When did voters repeal the tax on food and drugs?

A. 1944
B. 1964
C. 1974

**ANSWER: C**

In 1974, Michigan voters repealed the tax on food and drugs.

To drive, to fly, and to be a butcher, an electrician, or a plumber, you have to hold a license from the state of Michigan. Plumbers have been licensed for more than a century.

When did Michigan license the first woman plumber?

A. 1867
B. 1900
C. 1971

**ANSWER: A**

In 1867, Mary Ann Seadorf of Byron Center became the first women to be a licensed plumber in the state of Michigan.

Millions of people fly every year. It wasn't that long ago that flying on a vacation or a business trip was a rarity.

When did the first U.S. airline pass the 100,000-passenger mark?

A. 1919
B. 1929
C. 1949

When

In 1929, Stout Airlines, based at Ford Airport in Dearborn, became the first airline to fly more than 100,000 passengers. The airline opened in 1926, and it took three years to top 100,000 passengers. Stout Airlines later became part of United Airlines.

Today when we see trillion-dollar deficits and corporations making or losing billions of dollars in a year, it's hard to imagine when a billion dollars was a lot of money. The first corporation to make a billion dollars in a year was General Motors.

When did General Motors become the first corporation to earn a billion dollars in one year?

    A.  1947
    B.  1955
    C.  1967

**ANSWER: B**
The first corporation to earn a billion dollars was General Motors Corporation, in 1955.

To many people, a Christmas without a Christmas tree is like salt without pepper. The evergreen tree has become a symbol of the season. But it wasn't always so.

When did the first Christmas tree appear at the Vatican?

    A.  1688
    B.  1776
    C.  1982

**ANSWER: C**
In Italy, where most popes have been born for centuries, there is no tradition of Christmas trees. When the Polish Pope John Paul II became pontiff in 1982, he brought the tradition of a Christmas tree to the Vatican.

The Congressional Gold Medal is bestowed by the U.S. Congress and is, along with the Presidential Medal of Freedom, the highest civilian award in the United States. In its early years, before the

When

Congressional Medal of Honor was created, it was mostly presented to military heroes. It is given to an individual who performs an outstanding deed or act of service.

When did the first native of Michigan win the Congressional Gold Medal?

    A.  War of 1812
    B.  Spanish American War
    C.  WWII

**ANSWER: A**

Alexander Macomb, a hero of the American Revolution, was awarded the Congressional Medal of Honor for leading a small army of volunteers to a victory over the English in Plattsburg, New York, in 1814, during the War of 1812. Macomb was later the commander of the U.S. Army. Macomb County, Macomb Community College, and many other cities and towns are named for General Macomb.

They say the iron horse built America. The railroad was also very important in the development of the state of Michigan.

When was the first railroad company formed in the state of Michigan?

    A.  1830
    B.  1850
    C.  1867

**ANSWER: A**

In 1830, when not one mile of track existed in the United States, let alone Michigan, the Pontiac and Detroit Railway Company received its charter. Eight years later, the railroad finally began to operate.

Today we see aerial photos all the time, from traffic helicopters to people riding in planes. While those aerial photos are very common today, they were an amazing technology in the early years.

When was the first aerial photo published in a Michigan newspaper?

    A.  1912
    B.  1922

**When**

C. 1932

**ANSWER: A**
In 1912, a Detroit news photographer, riding in a hydroplane, took a picture of the Detroit waterfront.

You know about the Library of Congress. It is a collection of books and manuscripts housed in Washington, D.C. The state of Michigan also has a library in Lansing.

When was the Library of Michigan founded?

A. 1828
B. 1852
C. 1910

**ANSWER: A**
Before Michigan even became a state, the territorial legislature established the Library of Michigan in 1828 and hired a librarian at $100 a year.

The Red Cross is an organization that is famous for being the first relief agency on the job at a disaster site.

When did the Michigan chapter of the Red Cross first meet?

A. 1864
B. 1905
C. 1940

**ANSWER: B**
The first meeting of the Michigan chapter of the Red Cross took place in Detroit in 1905. Its first activity was collecting $65,000 for the relief of San Francisco after the Great Earthquake in 1906.

For years, girls in Michigan could get married at age 16 with the permission of their parents, but boys had to wait until they were 18.

When did Michigan law change so that both boys and girls could marry at age 16?

A. 1902
B. 1945

C. 1981

**ANSWER: C**
In 1981, Governor William Milliken signed a law that allowed boys to get married at 16 with their parents' permission, just like girls.

The Reverend Martin Luther King Jr. led marches all over the country in the search for justice. One of his biggest marches, the famous "Walk to Freedom," was held in Detroit.

When did Dr. King lead the "Walk to Freedom" march in Detroit?

A. 1958
B. 1963
C. 1968

**ANSWER: B**
In June of 1963, Martin Luther King Jr. led more than 125,000 marchers down Woodward Avenue in the "Walk to Freedom" demonstration.

It took women a long time to get their rights in the United States. Women couldn't even vote in Michigan until 1918, two years before the Nineteenth Amendment gave women the right to vote in the rest of the country.

When was the first woman elected to the Michigan Senate?

A. 1900
B. 1920
C. 1953

**ANSWER: B**
In 1920, the year women got the vote, Michigan voters sent Eva Hamilton to the state senate. She was the first woman to serve. She was a teacher born in Memphis, Michigan, in St. Clair County, in 1871. Hamilton was a Republican elected from Grand Rapids. She was defeated in a primary by a man and served from 1921 to 1923. She died in 1948, never having been elected to office again.

**When**

Just before WWI, Michigan saloons were forced by a new law to stop selling liquor on Sundays. This was one of the so-called blue laws that regulated alcohol sales. Bars and stores still can't sell alcohol before noon on Sundays.

When were bars in Michigan once again allowed to sell liquor on Sundays after noon?

    A.  1947
    B.  1955
    C.  1968

**ANSWER: C**
It wasn't until 1968 that state law allowed for liquor sales on Sunday after noon.

As most hunters know, there is a certain uniform you need to wear when hunting. It is hunter's orange, a color that really shows up in the woods. But hunters used to wear red.

When did the Michigan law that required hunters to wear orange take effect?

    A.  1957
    B.  1967
    C.  1977

**ANSWER: C**
In 1977, Governor William Milliken signed the law mandating that all hunters wear orange when in the field.

Michigan is known as a strong union state. It is the birthplace of the UAW and a strong supporter of the teamsters, AFL/CIO, MEA, and many more.

When was the first union in Michigan thought to have been formed?

    A.  1818
    B.  1900
    C.  1936

**When**

**ANSWER: A**
The Detroit Mechanics Society was organized in 1818 for their "mutual protection and benefit." In 1936, General Motors recognized the UAW as its workers' representatives.

The Michigan high school football playoffs began in 1975. Before that, a state champion team was a consensus pick. In some years, such as 1973, when Saginaw Arthur Hill went unbeaten and unscored on, it was easy. But in other years, where two or three great teams went undefeated, it was much more difficult.

When was the first consensus or "unofficial" Michigan state football champion selected?

    A.  1899
    B.  1925
    C.  1947

**ANSWER: A**
In 1899, Pontiac beat Plainwell 6-5 at Ann Arbor for the first "unofficial" state football championship. It was actually the first playoff, as the two teams were both undefeated, so they played each other to crown a champion.

The University of Michigan is Michigan's first university. It was founded in 1817.

When did the University of Michigan hold its first commencement?

    A.  1818
    B.  1845
    C.  1873

**ANSWER: B**
Though the U of M was founded in 1817, the first graduation ceremony was held in 1845. Eleven graduates received their degrees at Ann Arbor Presbyterian Church.

When

Wayne County was Michigan's first county, and it was a very large county. In 1796, Wayne County took in all of the state of Michigan and parts of Wisconsin.

When did Wayne County get its current boundary?

    A.  1800
    B.  1817
    C.  1826

**ANSWER: C**
After at least 12 configurations over 30 years, Wayne County got its current boundary in 1826.

Michigan is the auto capital of the world, the birthplace of the largest car companies.

When was Michigan's first automobile manufacturer organized?

    A.  1881
    B.  1899
    C.  1904

**ANSWER: B**
Michigan's first auto company was founded in 1899 and not by Henry Ford. The Detroit Automobile Company opened in 1899, built 20 vehicles, and closed.

Since the first state of Michigan historical marker was placed at the state capitol in 1957, hundreds more have been erected. They have honored Michigan residents, farms, businesses, bridges, and lighthouses—just about everything you can imagine. There is even one that is underwater!

When did Michigan place its first historical marker underwater?

    A.  1957
    B.  1974
    C.  1992

**ANSWER: C**
In August of 1992, the state of Michigan placed a historic marker at the bottom of Lake Huron in the Sanilac Underwater Preserve. It was placed at the site of the sinking of the tugboat *Sport*, which went down in 1920.

In 1861, a women's wing was added to the Detroit House of Corrections, where women convicts were sent to serve their time for many years.

When was the first prison built specifically for women convicts established in Michigan?

    A. 1917
    B. 1943
    C. 1977

**ANSWER: C**
In 1977, the state of Michigan built the $10-million Huron Valley Women's Facility at Ypsilanti.

Zoos are places where animals are confined within enclosures and displayed to the public and where they may also be bred to show and to even save a species. "Zoo" is short for "zoological garden." Many were started in ancient times when warriors would return from campaigns with treasure, slaves, and strange animals.

When did the world-famous Detroit Zoo open its doors?

    A. 1887
    B. 1912
    C. 1928

**ANSWER: C**
The Detroit Zoo opened on August 5, 1928. The zoo features more than 700 varieties of trees, plants, and shrubs and more than 1,200 animals. More than 260 are on the endangered species list. The word "zoo" was first used at the London Zoological Gardens, which opened for scientific study in 1828 and to the public in 1847.

When

Most of us in Michigan went to kindergarten when we first attended school but not all of us. Kindergarten is a fairly new concept. When did the first public schools in Michigan offer a kindergarten program?

    A. 1893
    B. 1927
    C. 1946

**ANSWER: A**
Although some private schools had a kindergarten as early as 1875, the first public schools to offer the program were in Grand Rapids and Detroit in 1893. By the turn of the century, most but not all public schools offered kindergarten. Today, most studies show that our children should start even earlier.

Michigan became a state in 1837 and had been part of the United States as a territory since 1805 and part of the new United States since the Treaty of Paris in 1783. But the British didn't leave the territory in 1796.
When did Michiganians vote for the first time?

    A. 1792
    B. 1824
    C. 1837

**ANSWER: A**
Residents of Michigan got to vote in 1792 but not in a U.S. election; they were voting as Canadians for representation at the Provincial Assembly of Upper Canada.

We've seen the movies and read the books about those Wild West train robberies by Jesse James and the like. Train robberies happened all over.
When was the last known train robbery in Michigan?

    A. 1884
    B. 1928
    C. 1953

**When**

Most believe that Amelia Earhart was the first licensed woman pilot because she's the only one they've heard of, after she was lost over the Pacific in 1937—but she wasn't.

When did the first woman get a pilot's license in the United States?

A. 1911
B. 1924
C. 1932

ANSWER: A
In 1911, Harriet Quimby became the first woman in the United States to earn a pilot's license. Quimby was born in Arcadia, Michigan, in 1875. She was the first woman to fly across the English Channel in 1912, but most never heard of her accomplishment because the day after her flight, the great ship *Titanic* sank on its maiden voyage.

Michigan citizens have been involved with flight since the beginning.

When did Michigan's first military air field open?

A. 1917
B. 1923
C. 1937

ANSWER: A
Selfridge Air Force Base in Mt. Clemmons opened in 1917. It was named for First Lieutenant Thomas E. Selfridge, an army flyer and the first person to die in a crash of a powered airplane. He was born in 1882 and graduated from West Point in 1903 with Douglas MacArthur. On September 17, 1908, Orville Wright went to Fort Myer to demonstrate the Wright Flyer for the U.S. Army, and Selfridge arranged to be a passenger while Orville piloted the craft. The engine broke, causing an accident that took Lieutenant Selfridge's life. Wright was severely injured but lived to tell the tale.

Baseball was made to be played outdoors under the sun, but owners discovered that paying fans could attend more games if they were at night, even though players couldn't see the ball as well.

When was the first night game played at Tiger Stadium?

    A.  1938
    B.  1948
    C.  1952

**ANSWER: B**
The Tigers won the first night game they played at home in 1948, a 4-1 victory over Philadelphia.

Flags symbolize countries, companies, teams, and states.

When was the current Michigan flag approved by the legislature?

    A.  1837
    B.  1911
    C.  1963

**ANSWER: B**
The Michigan flag, with the blue background and coat of arms, was approved in 1911.

    Michigan became a state in 1837, and the current state constitution was approved in 1963.

It used to be that an operator had to make calls for you; there was no such thing as direct dial.

When were the last operators in Michigan replaced with dial phones so customers could make their own direct-dial calls?

    A.  1958
    B.  1971
    C.  1980

**ANSWER: B**
In 1971, St. Ignace and Mackinac Island were the last places in Michigan to replace operators with dial phones.

Sports and television are a natural combination. The first home run seen on television was in the 1950s.

When was the first televised hole in one in golf?

 A. 1958
 B. 1962
 C. 1975

**ANSWER: B**
Jerry Barber shot the first hole in one seen on television in 1962 at the Buick Open at Warwick Hills Golf and Country Club in Grand Blanc Township. That year's Buick Open champion was Bill Collins.

When was the first Michigan-built horseless carriage featured in a national magazine?

 A. 1892
 B. 1907
 C. 1915

**ANSWER: A**
The first Michigan-built horseless carriage featured in a national magazine was a Ransom E. Olds steam engine automobile in 1892. It was in *Scientific American*.

Humans have been making wine and brewing beer for thousands of years. It is said that George Washington had his own beer recipe.

When did the first breweries appear in Michigan?

 A. 1798
 B. 1837
 C. 1901

"Let your fingers do the walking." That was the slogan for the yellow pages phone directories for many years. Today, many companies publish the directories.

When was the first yellow pages directory published in Michigan?

    A.  1906
    B.  1936
    C.  1946

Bounties on so-called nuisance animals have been paid for decades on everything from wolves and bears to beavers and coyotes.

When was the bounty on the last large animal repealed in Michigan?

    A.  1893
    B.  1947
    C.  1971

When was the last native wild turkey taken in a Michigan hunt?

    A.  1897
    B.  1958
    C.  1999

**ANSWER: A**
The last known native Michigan wild turkey was bagged in Van Buren County in 1897; they had been practically hunted to extinction. After that, turkeys from all over the country were brought to Michigan to reestablish wild turkeys in the state. The next wild turkey hunt in Michigan took place in 1965.

March Madness is the time of year around the country to watch college and high school basketball playoffs.

When was the first high school basketball champion crowned in Michigan?

    A.  1917
    B.  1947
    C.  1952

**ANSWER: A**
Michigan's first high school hoops state champ was crowned in 1917. Thirty-six teams had participated in Ann Arbor for the title. Detroit Northwestern High beat Jackson 24-21 to become the first Michigan high school basketball champion.

Among the very common nonnative species in Michigan are cows. Cows are not native to the state but have been there for a long time.

When were the first cows brought to Michigan?

    A.  1706
    B.  1776
    C.  1810

**ANSWER: A**
In 1706, 10 head of cattle and three horses arrived at Fort Ponchartrain in Detroit to help begin animal agriculture in the French fort.

Have you found yourself going faster than you thought down a highway? Speed limits get a lot of us in trouble, but there was a time when there were no speed limits on Michigan roads.

When did the state of Michigan enact its first speed limit laws?

A. 1925
B. 1932
C. 1956

**ANSWER: C**
The first speed limit wasn't posted until 1956. Before that, the speed limit was as fast as the driver could go. The first speed limit was 65 during the day and 55 at night.

On December 10, 1935, a very unlikely event took place in Michigan.
What happened in December of 1935?

A. Pigs flew at Bishop Airport in Flint.
B. The Detroit Lions won an NFL crown.
C. State legislators said no to a raise.

**ANSWER: B**
Believe it or not, the Detroit Lions won the NFL championship on December 10, 1935. They beat the New York Giants 26-7. They also won NFL championships in 1952, 1953, and 1957. They haven't won since.

Great Lakes storms are fearsome events. They often come in November, and some have been deadly and devastating.
When did the worst storm in recorded Great Lakes history take place?

A. 1913
B. 1937
B. 1975

**ANSWER: A**
The acknowledged worst Great Lakes storm began on November 9, 1913. The winds blew at hurricane force for 16 hours, and the storm lasted for three days. Forty ships were sunk and more than 235 sailors lost. Exactly 62 years later, another huge storm on the lakes sent the *Edmund Fitzgerald* to the bottom of Lake Superior.

**When**

The biggest college football rivalry in Michigan and one of the biggest in the nation is the famous Michigan–Michigan State game. The University of Michigan has a big lead in the overall series, but State has won some big ones. The biggest might have been the first win over a U of M team.

When did Michigan State beat Michigan in football for the first time?

    A.  1913
    B.  1938
    C.  1944

ANSWER: A

In 1913, when MSU was still known as the Michigan Agricultural College Aggies, they beat the mighty Michigan team 12-7. It was Michigan's only loss of that season. The teams played for the first time back in 1898.

The Upper Peninsula and Lower Peninsula of Michigan are connected by the Mackinac Bridge and a telephone cable.

When were the peninsulas connected by that phone line?

    A.  1889
    B.  1907
    C.  1938

ANSWER: A

The two peninsulas of Michigan were connected by a phone line in 1889.

Flint has been so connected to Buick Motors that its nickname is "Buick City." In May of 1999, the last Flint-made Buick rolled off the line at Buick City, thus ending an almost 100-year tradition of building Buicks in Flint.

When was the first Buick built in Flint?

    A.  1904
    B.  1908
    C.  1913

**When**

There have been hundreds of auto brands and thousands of dealers over the years. Recently, General Motors and Chrysler have been cutting dealerships to try to rebuild their networks. It has been a painful time all around, for the car companies and dealers alike. But auto dealerships and auto companies have been going under since the beginning of the auto industry. Names such as Nash, Rambler, Studebaker, and Hudson are historic notes.

When did the last Hudson dealer close its doors?

A. 1951
B. 1957
C. It didn't close.

**ANSWER: C**
Though the last new Hudson was built in 1957, there is still one Hudson dealer open for business in the country, Miller Hudson in Ypsilanti. Hudsons are still for sale, and parts, in authentic factory boxes, are still available. Miller Hudson opened its doors as a new car dealer in 1933.

When did the first African American doctor in Flint, Michigan, begin his practice?

A. 1918
B. 1942
C. 1951

**ANSWER: A**
The first African American doctor in Flint was probably Dr. John Wesly. He opened his office in 1918. In 1943, he became one of the founders of the Urban League of Flint.

When did Michigan State University play its first football game?

A. 1896
B. 1915
C. 1922

**ANSWER: A**
MSU played its first football game in 1896 as the Michigan Agricultural College Aggies. They played Lansing High School in that first game and won 10-0. George Wells of Ithaca scored all of the points in that game. They ended the season 1-2-1.

When did the first woman play in the U.S. Marine Corps Band?

A. 1957
B. 1973
C. 1986

**ANSWER: B**
In 1973, French hornist Sergeant Ruth Johnson of Saginaw, Michigan, became the first woman to be a member of the Marine Corps Band. Today, women comprise 30 percent of the band.

When

# "Why?"

## The great GREAT LAKES (*Why*) TRIVIA QUIZ

It's not often a president of the United States visits the state of Michigan, especially the Upper Peninsula. But in May of 1913, former President Teddy Roosevelt did visit Marquette for about a week.

Why did former President Teddy Roosevelt visit Marquette in 1913?

    A.  To hunt and fish
    B.  To go on a Great Lakes cruise
    C.  To file a lawsuit against a newspaper

**ANSWER: C**
Teddy Roosevelt had sued the *Marquette Newspaper* for libel after it reported he was habitually drunk. He won his case. The paper was fined 6 cents in damages and ordered to print a retraction and apologize.

There are many who believe in ghosts and hauntings, and let's face it, there are some eerie places.

Why do some believe that room 401 at Detroit's Grace Hospital is haunted?

    A.  A gangster was murdered there.
    B.  A magician died there.
    C.  It was built on an old burial ground.

**ANSWER: B**
On Halloween in 1926, the great magician Harry Houdini died in room 401 after his appendix ruptured. He promised his widow that if it was possible for the dead to contact the living, he would do it. So far, no word for Mr. Houdini.

It's been called the Motor City, Motown, and more for decades. Detroit has had other nicknames, too.

Why was Detroit once known as "Boneville"?

    A.  Its inhabitants were starving.
    B.  It had a bison bone–processing plant.
    C.  It was home to a trombone factory.

Why

**ANSWER: B**
Detroit was known as "Boneville" because from 1872 to 1900, the bones of bison were brought there by the ton to be processed into products such as fertilizer.

Why have some historians said that "to be a Michiganian is to be a little bit Canadian, too"?

    A.  We all live on the Great Lakes.
    B.  We all like hockey.
    C.  We were a province of Canada.

**ANSWER: C**
From the early 1600s until 1815, Canada ruled over a good portion of Michigan, so some historians do say we are all a bit Canadian, eh!

Have you ever heard of William A. Burt? He is a very important figure in Michigan and Great Lakes history. Burt was the state geologist and is the man believed to have discovered the Upper Peninsula's iron fields in 1846. He is also remembered for other important discoveries.

Besides discovering the iron fields of the U.P., why is William Burt remembered?

    A.  He invented the solar compass.
    B.  He invented America's first typewriter.
    C.  He discovered Lake St. Helen.

**ANSWER: A, B**
William Burt also invented the solar compass and America's first typewriter in 1829. A solar compass helps run straight lines through areas that have minerals that could affect regular magnetic compasses.

Stamping out forest fires is an important goal for conservation officials. But in Crawford County, they set fires every year.
    Why do they start forest fires in Crawford County, Michigan?

    A.  For farms
    B.  To see more deer
    C.  For birds to nest

**ANSWER: C**

The Kirtland warbler is a songbird that nests only in the Bahamas and in Michigan. The birds will nest only on the ground around young jack pines. But jack pines grow only after seeds are burned. So they set fires in Crawford County so there will be a place for the endangered Kirtland warbler to nest.

The Great Lakes have some very descriptive place names: Pictured Rocks, named for the colors of the rocks on the Superior Shore, and Sleeping Bear Dunes, for a Native American legend of a bear and her cub sleeping on the shore.

Why do they say the beaches at Grand Haven and Ferrysburg, Michigan, have "singing sands"?

A. They squeak if you walk barefoot.
B. The Sandpipers singing group started its career there.
C. The wind blows the sand.

**ANSWER: A**

The "singing sands" of Grand Haven and Ferrysburg squeak when you walk barefoot on the beach.

The University of Michigan has the wolverine as its mascot, and the state of Michigan is known as the Wolverine State.

Why is Michigan called the Wolverine State?

A. There are lots of wolverines there.
B. It was named by Ohioans.
C. It took the name from the university.

**ANSWER: B**

After the battle over the Toledo strip between Ohio and Michigan during the fight for Michigan statehood, Ohioans began to call people from Michigan wolverines, after the mean and vicious reputation of the animal. By the way, wolverines never really lived in Michigan, though a few have been found over the years after roaming in from other places.

A trip to Traverse City is a great vacation. The entire Grand Traverse County area is beautiful and one of the top tourist destinations in the Midwest. The area was first called Omeena.

Why

Why was the Traverse City area once called Omeena?

A. It was named for founder William Omeena.
B. It was a Native American word.
C. It was a nickname for mean lumberjacks.

**ANSWER: B**
Reverend Peter Doughtery was the area's first postmaster, and it is said that the name came from his response to any statement. He always answered any comment with "omeena," which was a Chippewa word for "is that so."

One of Michigan's displays at the Chicago World's Fair in 1893 was the largest stove ever built. It weighed 20 tons and stood 25 feet high.
Why did a stove represent Michigan at the 1893 Chicago World's Fair?

A. Detroit was a major stove manufacturer.
B. It was cold, and they needed a big stove.
C. They needed it to cook for the U.S. Army.

**ANSWER: A**
Once upon a time, before it became the Motor City, Detroit made more stoves than anywhere else on earth. Today the "Garland Stove" is on display at the Michigan State Fairgrounds after being restored in 1998.

Michigan residents played a prominent role in the Civil War. More than 90,000 soldiers fought and more than 14,000 died in the war to save the Union. Michigan has another claim to fame from the Civil War.
Why is Michigan remembered on the anniversary of the end of the Civil War?

A. Michigan troops accepted Confederate General Lee's surrender.
B. A Michigan senator told Lincoln the war was over.
C. Michigan troops captured Confederate President Jefferson Davis.

**ANSWER: A, C**
It was two Michigan regiments that accepted General Robert E. Lee's surrender at Appomattox, along with his army's flags and guns, and another that captured Confederate President Jefferson Davis as he tried to escape in women's clothes.

---

Fort Custer, near Battle Creek, Michigan, has been a military facility since 1917. It was chosen for two reasons. First, the area was easily accessible by railroad, but there was also a second reason.

Why was Battle Creek chosen as the site of Fort Custer?

A.   It was a dry county.
B.   It was close to manufacturing.
C.   Most recruits came from Michigan.

**ANSWER: A**
Military officials liked the railroad connections, but they really liked the idea that the area was dry and that draftees would have a hard time finding alcohol.

---

The Michigan state capitol building has a painting of Governor Austin Blair, Michigan's Civil War governor, and of the Marquis de Lafayette, hero of the Revolution. We know why Governor Blair's painting is there.

Why does Revolutionary war hero the Marquis de Lafayette have his portrait in the Michigan capitol building?

A.   He visited Michigan.
B.   The portrait of George Washington was stolen.
C.   He was beloved in Michigan for his Revolutionary War service.

**ANSWER: B, C**
Lafayette's portrait is featured at the Michigan state capitol because the portrait of General Washington was stolen and Lafayette was the last living general of the Revolutionary War. Lafayette did tour the country on the fiftieth anniversary of the revolution but never came to Michigan.

---

The interstate highway system is one of the crowning efforts of the Eisenhower administration in the 1950s.

Why is one mile in every five on interstate highways straight?

A. It saves gas.

B. It makes for a shorter distance.

C. So it can be used as an airstrip

**ANSWER: C**
General Eisenhower thought the straight areas of the highways could be used as airstrips in time of war or emergency.

Old Tiger Stadium, at the corner of Michigan and Trumbell, was a great place to watch a baseball game, but there was no parking there.
Why didn't Tiger Stadium have a parking lot?

A. It would help neighborhood residents make money.

B. The land was too expensive.

C. It didn't need a parking lot.

**ANSWER: C**
Tiger Stadium, or Navin Field at the time, didn't have a parking lot because it didn't need one. When it opened in 1912, few people owned a car; they rode the trolley or walked to the game.

The community of Ubly, in Huron County, was founded in 1865. Alfred Paggett owned a general store there, and the community was first called Paggett's Corners. It was renamed Ubly in 1880.
Why did they call it Ubly?

A. For Ubley, England

B. For Euby Johnson

C. For an ugly lumberjack

**ANSWER: A**
Ubly was named for Ubley, England. The station master at the train depot misspelled it, and it became the Village of Ubly, without an *e*.

In 1919, the coeds at the University of Michigan decided they would boycott dances because they were not allowed to use the Michigan Union. They ended their dance strike after just one week.

Why did the coeds at U of M end their dance strike after just one week in 1919?

A. They were allowed to use the Michigan Union.
B. They needed the exercise.
C. The men invited other girls.

**ANSWER: C**
After the men at the U of M announced that they would continue their dances with outside girls as guests, the women of Michigan decided to dance once again.

Farmers in the Great Lakes raise many animals: cattle, sheep, hogs, chickens, elk, horses, skunks . . . . That's right—a skunk ranch was founded near Monroe, Michigan, in the 1970s to raise descented and vaccinated skunks as pets. But in 1983, the farm was forced to move to the Upper Peninsula.

Why did the skunk farm have to move to the Upper Peninsula?

A. There were many neighbor complaints.
B. Skunks couldn't grow fast enough in Monroe.
C. Because of clean air standards

**ANSWER: C**
The skunk ranch was forced to move to the U.P. because of clean air standards but not because people were having trouble—the skunks were having trouble. Low air quality in the Monroe area was damaging the eyes, skin, and fur of the skunks.

Whether watching the health of lakes, streams, wildlife, or people, the state of Michigan has an obligation to pay attention. In 1928, two state of Michigan departments launched a program to control pollution to protect health.

Why did the Michigan Conservation Department and the Department of Health form a partnership to fight pollution?

A. To protect fish and people
B. The departments were housed in the same building.
C. The departments had the same director.

Why

**ANSWER: A**
Believe it or not, in 1928 the Michigan Conservation Department had more power to protect animals from contamination than the Health Department had to protect people. So they began to work together.

Back in 1928, officials in Livingston County, concerned with the morals of the day, passed a law that prohibited women from riding in a car while wearing a bathing suit. That law was quickly overturned by the State Highway Commission.

Why did they strike down the Livingston County law prohibiting women from wearing bathing suits in cars?

A. The commissioners liked women in swimming suits.
B. They said the county didn't have the authority.
C. Tourism officials said they'd lose business to Ohio, where women could wear anything.

**ANSWER: B**
In 1929, the attorney general decided that since the roads were controlled by the Highway Commission, a county didn't have the authority to ban women in swimsuits from riding in cars.

Alexis de Tocqueville, the French explorer and writer, visited Michigan in 1831. In his book *Democracy in America*, he describes visiting the frontier in Detroit and seeing a black bear used as a watchdog at John Todd's Tavern in Flint.

Why did de Tocqueville travel through Flint?

A. He wanted to trade for fur.
B. He got lost.
C. He was going to Saginaw.

**ANSWER: C**
When Alexis de Tocqueville arrived in Detroit in 1831, he wanted to see the real wilderness, so he asked where he should NOT go. He was told that Saginaw had only mosquitoes and fever and he should never go there. So, of course, that is exactly where he did go.

In spring, a great tradition around the Great Lakes is smelt dipping. The tasty little fish can be taken by dipping a net into the water as they are trying to come toward shore to spawn. One of the best places to dip smelt in Michigan is at a place called the "Singing Bridge," between Tawas City and Au Gres, on Saginaw Bay and Lake Huron. Why is it called the "Singing Bridge"?

A. A ghostly singer appears.
B. It was designed by William Singer.
C. It sings as you drive across.

**ANSWER: C**
The girder bridge that stood where old US 23 crosses the Au Gres River used to sound like it was singing as you drove across. That old bridge was removed in 1971 and replaced by a new and not very musical modern bridge. But while it no longer sings to us, it is still called the "Singing Bridge."

Michigan used to have many covered bridges. Today there are a few left, including some, like the bridge in Frankenmuth, that have been built recently to bring back that old look.
Why did people build covered bridges in the first place?

A. To get travelers out of bad weather
B. So horses wouldn't get spooked
C. To protect the bridges

**ANSWER: C**
Covered bridges were actually built to protect the actual bridges, not people or horses. A covered bridge protects the structure's underpinnings from rain, snow, and sun so it lasts longer. The covered bridge in Frankenmuth is a replica of the many covered bridges that once dotted Michigan's landscape.

December 30 is an important day in the history of Flint, as well as in the United States.
Why is December 30 so remarkable?

A. Founder Jacob Smith arrived.
B. General Motors was founded.
C. The "Sit-Down Strike" began.

Why

The University of Michigan's football stadium is one of the best known in the world. It is known as the "Big House."

Why is the U of M's football stadium in Ann Arbor called the Big House?

A. It was designed by Steve Bigger.
B. It was donated to the university by the Biggs family, where their family farm stood.
C. It holds the most spectators.

**ANSWER: C**
Michigan Stadium is called the Big House because it used to hold more spectators (107,501) than any other stadium. Currently, the stadium is the second largest in the United States, behind Penn State's Beaver Stadium, because of the reduction of 1,300 seats to make space available for people with disabilities. Michigan is still number one in attendance. As renovations continue, the capacity is expected to reach 108,000, once again making it the largest football stadium in the country. It is the fourth-largest stadium in the world. The record crowd at the Big House is 112,118 on November 22, 2003, when Michigan defeated Ohio State 35-21.

In many states, the state capital is in the state's largest city—but not in Michigan. Lansing is a fairly small city, and when it was founded, it was literally a wilderness.

Why did Lansing get to be the state capital of Michigan?

A. Detroit was too close to a foreign country.
B. Lansing is the center of the state.
C. Michigan State University was there.

**ANSWER: B**
Lansing was chosen to be the site of the state capital because it was centrally located. But the fact that Detroit, the first capital of Michigan, was on the border

with Canada was an issue. When Michigan gained statehood in 1837, it had been only a few years since the country had been at war with England and Canada.

Frankenmuth, Michigan, is one of the top tourist attractions in the world. Since the 1920s, the city's restaurants have served chicken dinners to travelers.

Why did Frankenmuth take up the famous Bavarian theme?

    A.  Everyone was from Germany.

    B.  It always looked that way.

    C.  I-75 was built seven miles away.

**ANSWER: C**

While it is true that many residents of the area around Frankenmuth were of German decent, the real reason the town took up the Bavarian theme was that I-75 had bypassed the city and it needed to attract visitors. It worked fabulously, and tens of thousands visit each year.

Michigan football has a rich history. It is the winningest college football team in history, played in the first Rose Bowl, and has been playing football for more than a century.

Why wouldn't legendary coach Fielding Yost allow his players to wear numbers on their jerseys until 1916?

    A.  He thought it interfered with teamwork.

    B.  Officials couldn't count.

    C.  Opponents couldn't count.

**ANSWER: A**

Coach Fielding Yost wouldn't allow his players to wear numbers because he believed it would interfere with teamwork. Coach Fielding Harris Yost was born in Fairview, West Virginia, in 1871. He was a lawyer, author, and businessman. He coached for 25 years at the University of Michigan and served as athletic director. He died in Ann Arbor in 1946 at age 75.

Legend says that the Republican Party first met "under the oaks" in Michigan. Also it's legend that in 1861 President Abraham Lincoln said, "Thank God for Michigan."

*Why*

Why did Abraham Lincoln say, "Thank God for Michigan"?

A. Michigan voted for him for president.
B. Michigan paid its taxes on time.
C. Michigan sent troops.

**ANSWER: C**

In May 1861, the federal government called for troops from all the states to fight the Civil War. When the first troops from a western state, Michigan, arrived in Washington, D.C., Mr. Lincoln was so relieved and grateful he is said to have greeted them saying, "Thank God for Michigan."

Playwright Arthur Miller has many connections to Michigan. The Pulitzer Prize–winning author, who was once married to Marilyn Monroe, graduated from the University of Michigan and spent time early in his career working in Flint, Michigan.

Why was Arthur Miller in Flint?

A. He was selling cars.
B. He was building cars.
C. He was working as a newspaper reporter.

**ANSWER: C**

Arthur Miller came to Flint in 1936 to write about the Great Sit-Down Strike that ended in the recognition of the United Auto Workers Union.

Why

# "How?"

## The great GREAT LAKES (*How*) TRIVIA QUIZ

All lakes, rivers, and streams flush themselves constantly. It's how they rid themselves of pollutants. A river might take a few days to flush; a lake could take months, years, decades, or even centuries.

How many years does it take for the water in Lake Michigan to completely change?

    A.  1 year
    B.  100 years
    C.  1,000 years

**ANSWER: B**

According to hydrologists, those who study water, it takes a relatively short 100 years to completely change the water in Lake Michigan.

---

In order to get to Lake Superior from Lake Michigan, you have to go through the Soo Locks in Sault Ste. Marie because the water is much higher on Lake Superior than on Lake Michigan.

How much higher above sea level is Lake Superior than Lake Michigan?

    A.  7 feet
    B.  13 feet
    C.  21 feet

**ANSWER: C**

Lake Superior is 21 feet higher than Lake Michigan.

---

Headed north on I-75 in Michigan, when you come to Standish in Arenac County, you know you have hit the "north country."

How did Standish get its name?

    A.  For its "standoffish" people
    B.  John D. Standish was an early settler.
    C.  Stanley Dish was a local lumberman.

**ANSWER: B**

John D. Standish of Detroit built a mill in Standish in 1871. The area was named Standish in his honor, except for about one year. While Mr. Standish was away

**How**

on business, the area was renamed Granton by the legislature in 1872. The next year, the name was changed back.

In most states, you have to be 21 to drink alcohol, 18 to vote, and usually 16 to get a driver's license.

How old do you have to be in the state of Michigan to be elected governor or lieutenant governor?

A. 21
B. 30
C. 36

**ANSWER: B**

To serve as governor or lieutenant governor in Michigan, you must be at least 30 years old. Michigan's first governor, Stevens T. Mason, would not have been eligible. Known as the "boy governor," Mason was the territorial governor of the Michigan Territory and later governor of the state of Michigan. Appointed acting territorial governor in 1834, he was just 22, and he was elected governor of the state at age 24. Mason is the youngest state governor in American history. In 1841, Mason moved to New York City, where, in January of 1843, he died of pneumonia at the age of 31.

Professional baseball games are getting longer to play, due to network commercials, replays, conferences on the mound, arguments from players and managers, and more.

How long did it take to play the shortest game in major-league history?

A. 1 hour, 13 minutes
B. 1 hour, 21 minutes
C. 1 hour, 33 minutes

**ANSWER: A**

In August of 1920, the Detroit Tigers shut out the New York Yankees 1-0 in 1 hour, 13 minutes.

Michigan place names often have a very interesting history. Saginaw is an unusual name.

How did Saginaw get its name?

A. It was a Native American word for "mouth of the river."
B. It was a Native American word that means "island that sags into the lake."
C. It was named for the place the Sauk tribe lived.

**ANSWER: A OR C**
There is some controversy here. The word "Saginaw" could be corrupted from the Native American for either "Sauk Place" or "mouth of the river." The debate rages on.

Ironwood is a city in the Upper Peninsula of Michigan. It is the home of MSU basketball Coach Tom Izzo and former Detroit Lions and San Francisco 49ers Coach Steve Mariucci. Ironwood was founded in 1885 as the commercial center of the Gogebic Iron Range.
How did Ironwood get its name?

A. From James "Iron" Wood
B. From its iron mines
C. From an iron used to make pancakes at a local tavern

**ANSWER: A**
Ironwood is named for prominent mine owner James "Iron" Wood.

Cars today can go very fast. Race cars can go 200 mph, and even your Chevy truck can hit 100+ mph. But speed is relative. The first vehicles available went up to 15 miles per hour, which once upon a time was very fast indeed. In 1904, Henry Ford took one of his vehicles onto frozen Lake St. Clair to see how fast it would go.
How fast did Henry Ford get his vehicle to go on Lake St. Clair in 1904?

A. 12 mph
B. 40 mph
C. 91 mph

**ANSWER: C**
In January of 1904, Henry Ford, in a publicity stunt, drove one of his vehicles more than 91 miles per hour on frozen Lake St. Clair.

The Les Cheneaux Islands are islands and channels on the Lake Huron shoreline on the southeastern tip of the Upper Peninsula of Michigan. The name is French for "the channels." The name is often corrupted to "the Snows."
How many islands are in the Les Cheneaux Islands?

    A.  10
    B.  36
    C.  52

**ANSWER: B**
There are 36 islands in the Les Cheneaux, some inhabited and some still unnamed. They are a very popular tourist destination, especially for boaters and kayakers.

Adrian is a college town and the seat for Lenawee County, situated on the Ohio border.
How did Adrian get its name?

    A.  From a woman business owner
    B.  From a Roman Emperor
    C.  From Adrian, New York

**ANSWER: B**
Adrian, which is in southeastern Michigan, was named for the Roman Emperor Hadrian by the wife of city founder Addison Comstock. Adrian was originally known as Logan.

Clarkston, whose real name is officially city of the village of Clarkston, is a small city located within Independence Charter Township in Oakland County.
How did Clarkston get its name?

    A.  From the Clark candy bar
    B.  It was pulled from a hat.
    C.  From the Clark brothers

ANSWER: C
The city of the village of Clarkston was named for brothers Jeremiah, Nelson, and Milton, who platted the village in 1840. Among Clarkston's most famous past residents are actress Valerie Bertinelli and Henry Ford, who maintained a summer home there.

The northern Michigan community of Oscoda is known for its summer festival, the Paul Bunyan Festival. It actually started in 1971 when community leaders discovered that the legend of that giant of a lumberman Paul Bunyan was born in their town.

How did Oscoda city leaders discover that the Paul Bunyan legend was born in Oscoda?

A.  From *Encyclopedia Britannica*
B.  It was written on a napkin found in a local museum.
C.  It was based on a local lumberjack named Paul Bunyan.

ANSWER: A
Believe it or not, they discovered that the *Encyclopedia Britannica* credited Oscoda native James McGillivary with the creation of the legend of Paul Bunyan. McGillivary was later a reporter for the *Detroit News-Tribune* when he wrote a story on July 24, 1910, about a heroic lumberjack of immense size and strength.

How

Baseball Hall of Fame Manager Sparky Anderson won World Series championships in the National and American leagues with the Cincinnati Reds and the Detroit Tigers. He also played in the major leagues.

How long did Sparky Anderson's career as a player last?

A.  1 year
B.  4 years
C.  7 years

ANSWER: A
Though Sparky Anderson was a great manager, as he would tell you, he was not a great player. He played only one year in the majors, with Philadelphia in 1959.

As people head to the north country of Michigan, they often pass through Bridgeport just off of I-75.

How did Bridgeport get its name?

A.  From the many bridges in the area
B.  From Bridgeport, Connecticut
C.  From John Bridge, village founder

**ANSWER: A**

Bridgeport got its name from the many bridges in the area. It was originally called Cass Bend, because of the bend in the Cass River there. It became Cass Bridge in 1864, and in 1880, it finally became Bridgeport.

The village of Snover, in Sanilac County, was founded in 1895.

How did Snover get is name?

A.  From U.S. Representative Horace G. Snover
B.  From the lots of snow it receives
C.  It was named for a songbird.

**ANSWER: A**

It was named for U.S. Representative Horace Greeley Snover. He was also a judge, an attorney, a school principal in Port Austin, and a banker. Snover was born in Romeo in 1847 and graduated from the University of Michigan in 1869 and the UM Law School in 1871. Snover was a Republican who served in Congress from 1895 to 1899. After leaving Congress, Snover moved to Port Huron, where he died at the age of 76 and is interred there in Lakeside Cemetery.

Every 10 years in the United States, the government conducts a census, or a count of how many people live in the country. In 1773, a census was taken at one of the largest settlements in the west, Detroit.

How many people were living in Detroit according to the census of 1773?

A.  372
B.  1,367
C.  5,127

224

**ANSWER: B**

Three years before the Declaration of Independence, the settlement at Detroit had 1,367 residents.

There has been a bridge at Zilwaukee, Michigan, for as long as we can remember. The drawbridge is remembered for backing up traffic on I-75 during the 1960s and 1970s. Later, the big bridge that replaced the drawbridge collapsed during construction. It is all open as of 2010.

How did Zilwaukee get its name?

A.   To confuse people
B.   It was named for Hans Zilwaukee.
C.   It was named for a province in Germany.

**ANSWER: A**

When Daniel and Solomon Johnson of New York came to the area in 1848, they built a sawmill. They named the area Zilwaukee hoping that German immigrants would confuse Zilwaukee with Milwaukee in Wisconsin.

We name roads for people, places, the place a road leads to, and even for hopes and wishes. Dixie Highway has been an important road in Michigan for generations.

How did Dixie Highway get its name?

A.   From Dixie Wells, the first woman driver in Oakland County
B.   From Dixie, as in the Old South
C.   It is an acronym for "**D**rive the **I**nterstate (**X**) across to **I**ts **E**nd."

**ANSWER: B**

In 1915, to mark 50 years of peace after the Civil War, the road was planned to help bring the North and South closer together. Dixie Highway ran from Miami, Florida, to Sault Ste. Marie, Michigan. While you can still find and drive on parts of the old Dixie Highway, it was mostly replaced by I-75.

Freeland in Saginaw County is the home of MBS International Airport.

How did Freeland get its name?

A. It had free land for settlers.

B. From Mammy Freeland, a local innkeeper

C. It was named for a city in Vermont.

**ANSWER: B**

Freeland was originally named Jay, for its first postmaster, Jefferson Jaqruth. But lumberjacks began to call the place Freeland after a local tavern owner named Mammy Freeland. The name became official in 1879.

The village of Dryden in Lapeer County is a small community of fewer than 900 residents. In 1953, Champion Homes, a manufacturer of recreational vehicles, was founded there. That company moved in the 1980s.

How did the village of Dryden get its name?

A. From "dryden," as in a dry or no-alcohol community

B. From poet John Dryden

C. It was named for a terrible drought in the area.

**ANSWER: B**

Dryden was named for the popular English poet John Dryden, who lived from 1631 to 1700. He dominated the literary life of Restoration England so much that the period came to be known as the Age of Dryden. Dryden's most famous resident was Major General George Owen Squier. He was born in Dryden in 1863, graduated from West Point, and received a Ph.D. from Johns Hopkins University in 1893. He wrote books and articles on the subject of radio and electricity. He invented what he called wired radio in 1922. It was a music service for businesses and subscribers over wires. Later, he changed the name to Muzak, which we still can hear today as "elevator music." Squier was instrumental in the establishment of the aeronautical division of the army, the ancestor of the U.S. Air Force, in 1907.

In 1892, the community of Rollo in Tuscola County, near Marlette, changed its name to Silverwood.

How did they come up with the name Silverwood?

A. From silver deposits

B. From Franz Silver, a jeweler

C. From a stand of trees

226

**ANSWER: C**

Silverwood was named for a stand of white pines in the area. When the residents first applied for a post office, they asked for something easy to remember. So, the government first called the area Easy, Michigan. It later became Rollo and then Silverwood.

Budget crises are a common event in Michigan. How to deal with them is the thing that changes every time. In 1908, Michigan's treasury was empty, and the state was not able to meet its payroll.

How did Michigan get out of that budget crisis?

A. All state employees were fired.
B. Railroads paid taxes in advance.
C. It declared bankruptcy.

**ANSWER: B**

In the 1908 state budget crisis, several railroads volunteered to pay $750,000 in taxes early to help the state get out of the mess.

Almont is a village in Lapeer County. The population was 2,803 at the 2000 census.

How did Almont get its name?

A. From General Almonte
B. From Al Mont, a local businessman
C. From Almont, Scotland

**ANSWER: A AND MAYBE C**

Almont was first settled in 1827 by James Deneen and got a post office in 1835 named Bristol, for Oliver Bristol, an early settler. Platted as Newburg in 1836, it became Almont in 1855. James Thompson, who donated the town clock that is still in the steeple at the First Congregational Church, supposedly proposed the name Almont in 1846 to honor Mexican General Juan Almonte. Others believe Thompson suggested Almont in honor of the region in his native Scotland. General Almonte was at the Battle of the Alamo, on the Mexican side. He is credited with sparing the life of the only two survivors (a woman and her daughter) at the Alamo.

How

The first settlers began to arrive in Saginaw County's St. Charles in 1852. By 1854, it had its own post office.

How did St. Charles, Michigan, get its name?

    A.   It was named for a church.

    B.   It was named for a village merchant.

    C.   It was named for the Prince of Wales.

**ANSWER: B**
St. Charles was named for Charles Kimberly, the first store owner in the village. It was said that Mr. Kimberly was such a fastidious and proper gentleman that he would never say a bad word. So the lumberjacks called him Saint Charles.

The Great Lakes are a superhighway to transport goods all over the world. The state of Michigan has several international seaports.

How many international seaports are in the state of Michigan?

    A.   2

    B.   5

    C.   12

**ANSWER: B**
There are five international seaports along the Michigan shoreline of the Great Lakes.
    Port Huron
    Bay City
    Sault Ste. Marie
    Detroit
    Muskegon

How many times did heavyweight boxing champion Joseph Barrow defend his crown?

    A.   10 times

    B.   16 times

    C.   25 times

How

**ANSWER: C**

Heavyweight boxing champion and Detroiter Joseph Barrow, better known as "the Brown Bomber" Joe Louis, defended his title 25 times.

The little village of Capac is in St. Clair County. It was founded by a group that moved up from Romeo, Michigan. One of the leaders of the settlers, a judge, chose the name for the area.

How did Capac, Michigan, get its name?

A. It was named for an Inca chief.
B. It was named for Judge Capac.
C. It was named for K-Pack Industries.

**ANSWER: A**

Judge Dewitt Walker named the village after Inca chief Huayna Capac, who died in 1627. No word on why or even how he had ever heard of the great South American chief.

William C. "Billy" Durant is the man who created General Motors in Flint a century ago. Durant was the definition of an entrepreneur; he created a lot of wealth and lost a lot as well. He lost control of the company he founded twice. The first time he got it back by building Chevrolet into a major car maker and using that to buy back his shares. The second time he lost it for good.

How much money did William C. "Billy" Durant lose when he lost control of GM for the last time in 1921?

A. $5 million
B. $15 million
C. $90 million

**ANSWER: C**

Durant lost his entire fortune of $90 million and control of General Motors in 1921. That's when $90 million was a lot of money. He lived on a small pension provided by Alfred Sloan and ran a bowling alley in Flint, Michigan, until his death in 1947.

How

Woodward Avenue in Detroit has been called Michigan's Main Street. It was first laid out in 1806 but is not mentioned on a map until 1825.

How did Woodward Avenue in Detroit get its name?

    A.  From Judge Augustus Woodward

    B.  Because it went into the woods

    C.  It led to the Woodward Lumber Mills.

**ANSWER: B, KIND OF . . .**

Judge August Woodward did lay out Woodward Avenue after the Great Fire of 1805. However, the judge always claimed that he did not name the thoroughfare for himself but had named it Woodward because it went toward the woods. Few people believed the future governor of Michigan.

The city of Auburn, in Saginaw County, was established in 1877 and became a city in 1947.

How did Auburn, Michigan, get its name?

    A.  From the auburn hair of a local woman named Lisa Tucker

    B.  From a poem

    C.  From John J. Auburn

**ANSWER: B**

Auburn was named from the first line of a poem by Irish poet Oliver Goldsmith. The poem is called "The Deserted Village." It begins: "Sweet Auburn, loveliest village of the plain."

    Lisa Tucker is from Lake Orion and is a friend and coworker of the author's wife. She is married and the mother of three. Her life is dedicated to her family and church. She does not have auburn hair.

The Great Lakes are the largest basin of freshwater in the world. Of Lakes Michigan, Superior, Erie, Huron, and Ontario, Lake Ontario is different.

How is Lake Ontario different from all of the other Great Lakes?

    A.  It is the shallowest.

    B.  It is the largest.

    C.  It is not in Michigan.

**How**

**ANSWER: C**

Lake Ontario is the only one of the Great Lakes that does not border the state of Michigan. Lake Erie is the shallowest, and Lake Superior is the largest. Lake Ontario is bounded by the Canadian province of Ontario, by Ontario's Niagara Peninsula, and by the state of New York.

If you love lighthouses, Michigan is the place to be. In Michigan, there is more shoreline than all but one other state, which makes the Great Lakes a place with lots of lighthouses and navigational lights.

How many lighthouses and navigational lights are there along Michigan's shoreline?

- A.  53
- B.  116
- C.  176

**ANSWER: B**

Most sources say that Michigan has 116 lighthouses and navigational lights. The first was built at Port Huron, at the mouth of the St. Clair River, so sailors could find it along the shore of Lake Huron.

**How**

Blumfield Corners, in Saginaw County, was founded by German immigrants who came to escape persecution.

How did Blumfield Corners and Blumfield Township get their names?

- A.  From wildflowers that grew there
- B.  From Robert Blum
- C.  From gunfighter Billy "One Bullet" Blum

**ANSWER: B**

The Germans came to America after Robert Blum was shot by the king's soldiers. They named the township in his honor in 1853. Blum was a German radical and member of the National Assembly of 1848. He was arrested during a stay in Vienna and executed, even though as a Member of Parliament he had diplomatic immunity. He became a martyr of the German revolution.

Joe Louis is considered the greatest boxer in the history of the sport. One way of determining his impact is to consider how long he held the heavyweight boxing championship.

How long did Joe Louis hold the heavyweight boxing title?

A. 4 years
B. 8 years
C. 11 years

**ANSWER: C**
Detroit's Joe Louis took the crown on June 22, 1937, and held it for 11 years, 8 months, and 7 days, the longest in history.

The Chevy Corvette—one of the classic sports cars of all time. The first was built in 1953, in Flint, and they continue to be built today in Bowling Green, Kentucky.

How many Corvettes were built in Flint in 1953?

A. 300
B. 3,000
C. 9,000

**ANSWER: A**
Only 300 of the classics were built in 1953. The oldest-known surviving 1953 Corvette, (serial number E53F001003, known as "double-o-three"), the third to come off the Flint assembly line, was sold in 2006 for $1 million. The oldest Corvette in existence is believed to be a preproduction prototype that was hand built and displayed at the 1953 GM Motorama in New York City. Another 1953 Corvette belonged to actor John Wayne. VIN #51 was delivered to Wayne on October 7, 1953. You can see the Duke's Corvette at the National Automobile Museum in Reno, Nevada.

In the Upper Peninsula county of Luce, there is a quaint little community called Dollarville. It grew up around a mill and a general store.

How did Dollarville get its name?

A. From Bob Dollar, the local store manager
B. From a local who gave silver dollars to children
C. From the first dollar spent at the local saloon

How

Under the heading "It takes all kinds," in 1964 an 18-year-old man set a record for flying from a kite across Lake Michigan.

How long did it take him to cross Lake Michigan suspended below a kite?

    A.   3.5 hours

    B.   8 hours

    C.   15 hours

**ANSWER: A**

David Rude, suspended below a 14 × 16-foot kite, behind a 17-foot 200-horsepower motorboat, made the 81-mile trip across Lake Michigan in 3.5 hours.

Historians say that the first European to see Michigan was a Frenchman named Etienne Brulé in 1620. At that time, the only people in Michigan were Native Americans.

According to estimates, how many Native Americans were living in Michigan in 1620?

    A.   1,000

    B.   15,000

    C.   50,000

**ANSWER: B**

Historians estimate that when Etienne Brulé arrived in what is now Michigan in 1620, there were around 15,000 Native Americans living there.

Automobiles have been manufactured in Michigan since the turn of the twentieth century. Buick began to make cars in 1904, Oldsmobile in 1902, and Ford in 1903.

How many vehicles were registered in Michigan by 1913?

A. 5,000
B. 15,000
C. 60,000

**ANSWER: C**
In 1913, approximately 60,000 vehicles had been registered in Michigan.

When people were first settling the Saginaw Valley in Michigan in great numbers in the 1830s and 1840s, they came because land in Michigan was "fertile, plentiful, and cheap."

How cheap was land in the Saginaw Valley in the 1830s and 1840s?

A. 50 cents an acre
B. $1.50 an acre
C. $3 an acre

**ANSWER: B**
Land in mid-Michigan was selling for as little as $1.50 an acre.

The Mackinac Bridge was designed to sway with the wind. That is important because there is a lot of wind at the Straits of Mackinac. How far was the Mackinac Bridge designed to sway off center?

A. 3 feet
B. 8 feet
C. 27 feet

**ANSWER: C**
The Mackinac Bridge was designed to sway 27 feet off center. It has never been fully deflected but does move with a strong wind. It would take a 150-mile-per-hour wind several hours to slowly deflect. It would then take several more hours for Big Mac to get back to normal.

Belle Isle, in the Detroit River, was originally named Hog Island. It got that name because wild boars lived on the island years ago.

How did Hog Island become Belle Isle?

A.  Because of the big bell that was sounded on the island
B.  It was named for the island's owner, Jacque Belle.
C.  From ladies who visited the island

**ANSWER: C**
Hog Island was renamed Belle Isle on Independence Day 1845 in honor of the lovely ladies who visited the island. The city of Detroit purchased the island in 1879 and made it into a city park.

As you head north in Michigan, you may go to the resort town of Cadillac, in Wexford County.
How did Wexford County get its name?

A.  From Wexford County, Ireland
B.  From William and Xavier Wexford, lumber mill owners
C.  From Dr. Ira Wexford, the first area doctor

**ANSWER: A**
Wexford County, Michigan, was named for Wexford County, Ireland. The county was organized in 1869, with the county seat in Sherman. The county seat was moved to Cadillac in 1882, and it remains there to this day.

Interlochen, a small community near Traverse City, is mostly known for the Interlochen Center for the Arts.
How did Interlochen get its name?

A.  From a city in Sweden
B.  It is located between two lakes.
C.  It was named for a locksmith.

**ANSWER: B**
Interlochen got its name by being situated between two lakes, Duck and Green. The Odawa tribe lived between those lakes, which they called Wahbekaness and Wahbekanetta. Logging and fishing became big businesses in the 1800s until 1917, when the state of Michigan bought the remaining virgin pine and created Interlochen State Park, the first state park in Michigan. In 1928, the National Music Camp was founded at Interlochen; it became Interlochen Center for the Arts.

Lake Orion, in Oakland County, has a GM plant, golf courses, and a state park.
How did Lake Orion get its name?

A. From the star constellation
B. From Margaret O'Brien
C. Because it sounded nice

**ANSWER: C**
Lake Orion was first called Canandaigua by the settlers who came from New York State. The name was changed to Lake Orion in 1859 because some felt it was "short, handy to write, and altogether lovely."

Hammerberg Road is an important thoroughfare near downtown Flint.
How did Hammerberg Road in Flint get its name?

A. From a military hero
B. From the hammer used by auto workers
C. From a town in Germany

**ANSWER: A**
Hammerberg Road was named to remember Owen Francis Hammerberg. He was awarded the Congressional Medal of Honor, posthumously, for saving two divers at Pearl Harbor on February 17, 1945. He is the only Medal of Honor winner who was honored for action that was not in combat. In the aftermath of the attack on Pearl Harbor, navy divers had to clear dangerous debris. Hammerberg, a diver himself, rescued a diver who was trapped under a sunken LST. After this rescue, he went back, even farther under the buried hulk, and rescued a second diver. This time, however, he was pinned down himself by another cave-in and died.

Street names in local communities are very interesting. They are named for people, places, and sometimes things.
How did Beach Street in downtown Flint get its name?

A. It was named for the trees along the street.
B. It was named for a Revolutionary War veteran.
C. It was named for a sand beach along the Lake Huron shore.

**ANSWER: B**

Beach Street in Flint was named for Jonathon Beach, a Revolutionary War veteran who came to Flint in 1835 to live with his daughter.

Flint's Bishop International Airport has become an important air hub to the world.

How did Bishop Airport get its name?

    A. From the Catholic bishop of Lansing

    B. From Crash Bishop, Michigan's first licensed pilot

    C. From a local banker

**ANSWER: C**

Bishop Airport is named for Arthur Giles Bishop, who donated 220 acres of land at Torrey and Bristol roads for one of the first airports in the country. Today, Bishop includes more than 1,000 acres. Arthur Bishop was born in 1851. He went to Flint schools and graduated from the University of Michigan in 1873. He started as a clerk at Citizens' National Bank and later worked at the Genesee County Savings Bank. By 1912, he was president of the bank. Bishop was instrumental in the development of General Motors Corporation and orchestrated the move of C. S. Mott and his company to Flint in 1905. Bishop was director of the Buick Motor Company in 1905 and on the board of directors of General Motors from 1915 until his death in 1944.

**How**

In 1913, the *Flint Journal*, in an editorial, said, "The angel of death is on the back of every fly." The paper went on to offer to pay residents for every 1,000 flies they brought into the *Journal* offices.

How much did the *Flint Journal* offer to residents for 1,000 flies?

    A. 25 cents

    B. $5

    C. $7.50

**ANSWER: A**

The *Flint Journal* offered 25 cents for 1,000 flies brought in by readers. It believed the plan would cut down on the flu and other diseases.

The Irish Hills in Jackson County are a beautiful part of the state of Michigan.
How did the Irish Hills get their name?

A. From shamrocks
B. They looked like Ireland.
C. From Irish whiskey distilled there by moonshiners

**ANSWER: B**
The Irish Hills got their name when a small colony of Irish immigrants settled the area. The hills and 62 lakes in the area reminded them of the Emerald Isle. It is the home of Michigan International Speedway.

Michigan's first county was Wayne County. It was a large county, taking in most of Michigan and parts of Ohio, Illinois, and Wisconsin.
How did Wayne County get its name?

A. From an American general
B. From an English trapper
C. From Wayne McComb, an early settler

**ANSWER: A**
Wayne County, Michigan, and dozens of other counties and cities around the country, was named for General Anthony Wayne. General Wayne was born in Chester County, Pennsylvania, and was a Revolutionary War general. He was known as "Mad" Anthony Wayne because of his legendary temper.

How did Flint get the nickname "Vehicle City"?

A. From the carriage industry
B. From General Motors plants
C. It was the home of Buick.

**ANSWER: A**
Flint was the center of the carriage industry and was one of the largest manufacturers of carriages in the world. Many of the original carriage factories were later turned into auto factories as Flint became one of the largest manufacturers of automobiles in the world.

How did Tuscola County get its name?

A.  It was named for an Indian chief.
B.  It was named for a city in New York.
C.  The name was just made up.

**ANSWER: C**
The name Tuscola was made up by Henry Schoolcraft because it sounded like a Native American word. Schoolcraft, born in 1793, was an Indian agent, geographer, geologist, and ethnologist who made a great study of Indian languages. He named many places in Michigan using Indian words, and some he just made up, such as Tuscola, Alcona, Allegan, Alpena, Arenac, Iosco, Kalkaska, and Oscoda. In his spare time, he discovered the source of the Mississippi River in 1832. He married Jane Johnston, who was part Ojibwa. Schoolcraft and his wife were instrumental in providing material for Longfellow's epic poem "The Song of Hiawatha."

When winter comes to the Great Lakes, you can see a lot of snow. How much snow fell in Ishpeming, Michigan, on January 25, 1922, to set a record in Michigan for snowfall in one day?

A.  22 inches
B.  29 inches
C.  34 inches

**ANSWER: B**
On January 25, 1922, in the Upper Peninsula city of Ishpeming, a little more than 29 inches of snow fell, setting a record. Even if it hadn't been a record, it was a huge amount of snow.

NASA has a remarkable record of safety, considering that it sends human beings into orbit. There have been two major disasters in the space program. The most recent was the space shuttle disaster in 1986, when space shuttle *Challenger* broke apart 73 seconds into its flight, leading to the deaths of its seven crew members. There was another. In 1967, three astronauts were killed in a flash fire aboard *Apollo 1*.

How is Michigan connected to the *Apollo 1* disaster?

How

A. The *Apollo 1* spacecraft was built in Michigan.
B. The mission was designed in Michigan.
C. One of the astronauts was from Michigan.

**ANSWER: C**
Roger Chaffee, from Grand Rapids, Michigan, was one of the astronauts who died. He, along with Gus Grissom and Edward White III, were in the *Apollo* module on the tarmac when a flash fire killed all three on January 27, 1967.

When you visit Port Austin, Michigan, at the tip of Michigan's Thumb, you will note a big house that is today a bed and breakfast. It is the Garfield Inn.
How did the Garfield Inn get its name?

A. It was named for a U.S. congressman.
B. It was named for the local lumberman who built it.
C. It was named for a village in England.

**ANSWER: A**
It was named for Congressman, later President, James Garfield, the twentieth president of the United States. His assassination six months after his inauguration made his tenure, as president for 199 days, the second shortest (after William Henry Harrison) in history. He was succeeded by Chester A. Arthur. He was a major general in the U.S. Army during the Civil War and a member of the U.S. House of Representatives. Garfield was the second U.S. president to be assassinated; Abraham Lincoln was the first. To date, Garfield is the only sitting member of the House of Representatives to have been elected president. A family friend of the owners, he stayed at the inn several times during the 1860s and even gave a speech from the balcony of the inn endorsing General U. S. Grant for president.

How did Bad Axe, Michigan, get its name?

A. It was named for an Indian chief.
B. It was named for a hatchet fight.
C. It was named for an ax found in an old cabin.

**ANSWER: C**
While surveying a road in 1861, a surveyor named Captain Rudolph Papst found a much-used, long-forgotten ax in an old hunter's cabin. In his report on the area, he used the name Bad Axe to describe the place, and the name stuck. So Bad Axe really was named for a bad ax.

If you're in Michigan's Upper Peninsula and decide you want to get that holiday feeling, you might decide to stop in Christmas, Michigan.
How did Christmas get its name?

    A.  It's Santa's hometown.
    B.  It was settled on Christmas Day.
    C.  It was the site of a gift factory.

**ANSWER: C**
It was named Christmas because Julius Thorson bought some swampland in 1938 to build a factory to make Christmas gifts. He named it Christmas with marketing in mind. In 1940, the factory burned down, but the name stuck.

How did the Macomb County village of Disco get its name?

    A.  It is the Latin word for "learn."
    B.  It was named for John Disco, the village founder.
    C.  It was named for the music of the 1970s.

**ANSWER: A**
Disco was named by a local school teacher for the Latin word meaning "learn." The teacher arrived in the area in 1849 and opened a school he called the Disco Academy.

How did the Van Buren County community of Paw Paw get its name?

    A.  It was the home of some dogs with big paws.
    B.  It was named for a fruit.
    C.  The first postmaster's son called him Paw Paw.

How

**ANSWER: B**
Paw Paw was named by local Native Americans for the paw paw trees that used to grow along the Paw Paw River. Paw paw trees don't grow as well there anymore because they need shade to grow and the shade trees have mostly been cut down.

There are few ancient rock paintings in Michigan, probably because the environment is not conducive to paint and carvings. There are some ancient petroglyphs in Sanilac County in Michigan's Thumb region.
How were the Sanilac petroglyphs discovered?

    A.  Miss Simon's third-grade class found them on a field trip.
    B.  Artist Pamela Ruschman found them while painting a woods scene.
    C.  After a forest fire

**ANSWER: C**
They were discovered after a forest fire in 1881. The fires burned away the brush and grass along the Cass River and exposed the ancient art. There are more than 100 figures, designs, animal tacks, and birds depicted. Sanilac Petroglyphs Historic State Park was created to protect the only known rock carvings attributable to Native American Indians in Michigan. Geologists believe the carvings were made 300 to 1,000 years ago.

    Pam Ruschman is a friend of the author and is a well-known artist from Mequon, Wisconsin, whose work is shown throughout the Great Lakes.

How did Port Hope, Michigan, on the shores of Lake Huron in the Thumb of Michigan, get its name?

    A.  From the hope to sell land
    B.  From being thankful to get on land
    C.  From the hope to survive another winter

**ANSWER: B**
In 1857, Mr. William Southard, a partner of town founder William Stafford, and Mr. Witcher were traveling to the area by schooner. Because of a coming storm, they were let off at some distance from shore. Rowing the skiff in the wind, they vowed that if they made shore, they would name the spot Port Hope.

How did the unusually cold winter of 1936 change the little town of Cedar Springs, Michigan?

    A.  It changed the course of Cedar Creek.

    B.  There were more weddings there.

    C.  It created a market for underwear.

**ANSWER: C**

That cold winter of 1936 created a new market for red flannel underwear. A New York newspaper published an editorial that said, "Here we are in the midst of an old fashioned winter and not a red flannel in the country." The Cedar Springs paper answered with an editorial of its own that said "Saks may not have red flannels but we have plenty here in Cedar Springs." That editorial was picked up in papers all over the country and caused a new market for red flannels that the good folks in Cedar Springs, Michigan, were only too pleased to fill.

Michigan is known as the winter water wonderland. There are a lot of lakes and streams there.

How many waterfalls are there in Michigan?

    A.  12

    B.  87

    C.  150

**ANSWER: C**

Michigan has at least 150 waterfalls; the most famous is Tahquamenon Falls near Paradise in the Upper Peninsula. As a matter of fact, 148 of those waterfalls are in the Upper Peninsula.

How did the Manitou Islands in Lake Michigan get their name?

    A.  From a Native American word meaning "spirits"

    B.  They were named after an early French trapper.

    C.  From two men who owned the island

**ANSWER: A**

The Manitou Islands were named for the Native American word for "spirits." Legend says that sailors who approached the islands saw mirages and the island seemed to change shape and disappear.

How

Pinconning in Bay County in northern Lower Michigan is known for Pinconning cheese.
How did Pinconning get its name?

A. From manufactured pins
B. From the German word for "cheese maker"
C. From the Native American word for "potato"

**ANSWER: C**
Pinconning is an Algonquin word for "potato." The local Ojibwa tribe gave the name to the river where wild potatoes grew. The community is known for its namesake Pinconning cheese. It's an aged yellow Colby-style cheese developed by Dan Horn in 1915. Because of that, Pinconning is the cheese capital of Michigan.

The world-famous Munger Potato Festival is held every summer in Bay County's Munger.
How did Munger get its name?

A. It was the name of land owners.
B. From a local plant eaten instead of potatoes
C. From the French word for "hungry"

**ANSWER: A**
Munger was named for brothers Curtis and Algernon Munger from Bay City. They owned all the land surrounding the railroad depot. Founded in 1874, Munger has been celebrating its potato crop with a festival since 1954.

Empire is a village in Leelanau County situated in the Sleeping Bear Dunes National Lakeshore Park along the shores of Lake Michigan.
How did Empire get its name?

A. It was named for New York, the Empire State.
B. It was named for the Roman Empire.
C. It was named for a ship stuck in the ice.

**ANSWER: C**

The village of Empire is believed to have been named after the schooner *Empire*, which went aground and was stuck in the ice in 1865. It served as the village school that winter. First settled in the mid-1850s by John La Rue, it later became a center for lumbering, with its population reaching 1,000 by 1900. The last mill burned in 1917 and ended the Empire lumbering era. Today, the village is a tourist destination.

## How did Detroit make telephone history?

A.  It had the first phones.
B.  It had the first phone numbers.
C.  Telephones were invented there.

**ANSWER: B**

By the year 1879, the city of Detroit had so many phone customers it became the first place in the country to assign phone numbers.

## How did Chesaning, in Saginaw County, get its name?

A.  It was named for a big rock.
B.  It was named for the Chessin family.
C.  It was founded by a group of chess players.

**ANSWER: A**

Chesaning is a Native American (Ojibwa) word for the sacred big rock that was in the Shiawassee River at the site. Unfortunately, the rock no longer exists. The first European settlers blasted and burned it to make lime. Chesaning is known for its July Showboat Festival, founded in 1937. It is a festival and concert series in the Vaudeville style.

## How did Huron County's village of Caseville get its name?

A.  From landowner Leonard Case
B.  From a case of rum found on the beach
C.  From a famous court case

**How**

**ANSWER: A**

Caseville was named for Leonard Case in 1856 when he sold 20,000 acres of land to Francis Crawford. Crawford became the first postmaster of the village. The first settler was Ruben Dodge, who brought his family from Maine in 1836. The area was first called Pigeon River and later Port Elizabeth or Elizabethtown, for the wife of William Rattle, who represented Mr. Case before he sold the property.

Hush Puppies are a very popular brand of shoes for men and women. The company is based in Rockford, Michigan, and was founded there in 1858 as the Krause Tannery.

How did Hush Puppies get their name?

    A.  The owner had quiet dogs.

    B.  They were named for Southern corn balls.

    C.  They were named for designer Pap Hushman.

**ANSWER: B**

Hush Puppies were named by an ad man named Gaylord Muir. When he met with a company salesman for dinner, they had hush puppies, deep-fried corn balls. When Muir asked how they got that name, he was told farmers threw hush puppies at the hounds to "quiet their barking dogs." In a eureka moment, he decided his new shoes were so comfortable that they could "quiet barking dogs" (feet). The secret to Hush Puppies' soft feel is that they are made with pig skin instead of cowhide. Hush Puppies claim that their shoes' rubber soles saved the life of rolling Stones guitarist Keith Richards when he touched his guitar to an ungrounded microphone at a 1965 concert in Sacramento, California. He was knocked out cold, and medics say the Hush Puppies shoes that Richards was wearing insulated him.

The hometown of one of the great universities in the world, the University of Michigan, is Ann Arbor, Michigan.

How did Ann Arbor get its name?

    A.  From a woman named Ann Arbor

    B.  From an arbor celebration

    C.  From the names of the founders' wives

How

**ANSWER: C**
Ann Arbor was named in honor of the wives of the founders of the community and the grove of trees in the area. The women named Ann were Ann Allen, wife of John from Virginia, and Ann Ramsey, wife of Walker of New York. Both families arrived in 1823.

Lots of people have played major-league baseball, big ones and little ones, tall and short.

How tall was the shortest man ever to play in a major-league game?

    A.  3'7"
    B.  4'3"
    C.  5'

**ANSWER: A**
In August 1951, St. Louis owner Bill Veeck needed to make a splash, publicity wise. He also wanted a win! He signed 3'7" Eddie Gaedell and had him bat in game 2 of a doubleheader against the Detroit Tigers. Gaedell, wearing number 1/8, walked on four pitches, and the Tigers won the game 6-2. As a result of Gaedell's appearance, all contracts must now be approved by the commissioner of baseball before a player can appear in a game.

How did Tahquamenon Falls, near Paradise, Michigan, in the Upper Peninsula, get its name?

    A.  From a Chippewa word for "dark water"
    B.  From a Finnish word for "red water"
    C.  From a fake Native American word made up by Henry Schoolcraft

**ANSWER: A**
The name Tahquamenon is a Native American word meaning "dark water," which is the result of leaching of tannic acid from the cedar and hemlock swamps that feed the river. It also may have had something to do with an island in Whitefish Bay, Tahquamenon Island. The name Outakouaminan appears on a 1671 French map. The Tahquamenon River is mentioned in Longfellow's poem "The Song of Hiawatha." Tahquamenon is second only to Niagara Falls as the largest waterfall east of the Mississippi.

How

Michigan is the Great Lakes State.
How many lakes over 10 acres in size are there in Michigan?

A. 897
B. 4,763
C. 11,037

ANSWER: C

There are at least 11,037 lakes larger than 10 acres in Michigan. No wonder Michigan is the "water wonderland."

How did the city of Alma, in Gratiot County, get its name?

A. From General Hasting A. Alma
B. From Alma Ely
C. From Al Maha, village founder

ANSWER: B

The city of Alma was most likely named for Alma, the daughter of the community's founder, General Ralph Ely. Ely founded what was then called Elyton and built a sawmill in 1854. He was the first postmaster in 1857 and Alma's first village president. In August 1861, he raised a company of troops to fight the Civil War and was made captain. He ended the Civil War as a colonel. He was elected to the Michigan Senate in 1873 and for a time was Michigan's auditor general, which is why he is also referred to as General Ely. He died in Emmett County in 1883 and was buried in Alma in the cemetery next to the Pine River, a short distance from where he built his sawmill years earlier.

It used to be that we could look forward to retiring at age 60 or 65. That age continues to creep up for us today.

How old was the oldest employee ever to work for Ford Motor Company?

A. 77
B. 87
C. 97

ANSWER: B

William Perry, an African American, went to work for Mr. Ford in 1914 and was still on the payroll when he passed away at age 87. Perry was also the first African

American to work at Ford. Despite bad health and advancing age, Perry was kept on at Ford because at the bottom of his employment application, Henry Ford wrote, "Mr. H. Ford is interested in this party."

How did the little community of Shaftsburg, in Shiawassee County, get its name?

A. From John P. Shaft
B. From a movie character
C. From a bad land deal

**ANSWER: A**
Shaftsburg was named for the owner of the land it was built on. John P. Shaft, the land owner, not the movie character, bought the land in 1846, platted the area, and built the area's first hotel.

During WWII, many great baseball stars joined the service. Ted Williams, Joe DiMaggio, and Hank Greenberg all went to war. Hank Greenberg was a Detroit Tiger MVP who left the Tigers in 1941 to join the army.

How did Hank Greenberg celebrate going off to war and his return?

A. He sat out games.
B. He went to a worship service.
C. He hit home runs.

**ANSWER: C**
In Hank Greenberg's last game before going into the army, May 6, 1941, he blasted two home runs, leading the Tigers to a 7-4 win over the Yankees. When he returned on July 1, 1945, he hit another home run to celebrate.

How did the little village of Hadley, in Lapeer County, get its name?

A. From Reverend Franklin Hadley, postmaster
B. From Hadley J. Lapeer, founder of Lapeer
C. From Hadley, Ohio

**How**

**ANSWER: A**
The community was named for the area's postmaster, Reverend Franklin Hadley, who took his position in 1907. For the next 50 years, a member of the Hadley family served as the postmaster of the community.

## How did Oakland County get its name?

A. From Jack Okie, singer/actor
B. From oak trees
C. From the okra crop

**ANSWER: B**
Oakland County, founded by Territorial Governor Lewis Cass in 1819, was named for the many stands of oak trees in the area.

## How did Menominee, in the Upper Peninsula, get its name?

A. From the Native American word for "rice"
B. From the nickname for an Irish mother
C. From Justice Marland E. Menonimee

**ANSWER: A**
Menominee gets its name from a Native American word that means "wild rice" or "rice eaters." A local tribe is also known as the Menominee, or "those that eat rice."

There have been political arguments about the length of prison sentences in Michigan for many years. How long does life in prison mean? What is a reasonable sentence for grand theft?

How many years did Michigan's longest-serving inmate serve?

A. 45 years
B. 56 years
C. 61 years

**ANSWER: B**
In 1914, 21-year-old Casa Nostra was convicted of murder and sentenced to life in prison. He stayed behind the walls of Jackson Prison for 56 years before Governor William Milliken commuted his sentence in 1970 when he was 77 years old.

People have been finding ways to cross Lake Michigan for centuries.

How did Victor Jackson get across the Great Lake in 14 1/2 hours in 1969?

    A.  By rowboat

    B.  By swimming

    C.  By bathtub

**ANSWER: C**

In August 1969, Victor Jackson completed his 14 1/2-hour, 65-mile journey across Lake Michigan in a bathtub. His regular ole bathtub was powered by a 20-horsepower outboard engine. He landed in Manitowoc, Wisconsin.

How did Kent County, on Michigan's west side, get its name?

    A.  From Kent McVittie, local trapper

    B.  From Judge James Kent

    C.  From Kent, England

**ANSWER: B**

Kent County was named for Judge James Kent, a New York jurist and legal scholar who represented the Michigan Territory in its dispute with Ohio over the Toledo Strip.

    Kent McVittie is a Scout friend of the author.

Ferris State University started in some rented rooms over a bank in Big Rapids, Michigan. It was a private college that became a state university.

How did Ferris State University go from being a private college to a state university?

    A.  It was donated to Michigan.

    B.  Michigan bought it.

    C.  It went bankrupt and Michigan took over.

**ANSWER: A**

In 1949, the Ferris Institute was donated to the state of Michigan by its board of directors. It was named for its founder, Woodbridge N. Ferris, who became

How

governor of Michigan in 1912. Ferris was an educator from New York and also served as a U.S. senator from Michigan. He died in office in Washington, D.C., in 1928.

One of the great feats of engineering in history is the building of the Mackinac Bridge. Big Mac was completed in 1957. Before the bridge, people got across the Straits of Mackinac via ferry.

How many vehicles took the ferry across the Straits of Mackinac the year before the Mackinac Bridge opened for business?

    A.  50,000
    B.  540,000
    C.  800,000

**ANSWER: C**
In 1956, the last year of ferrying cars across the straits, 800,000 cars were transported to the Upper Peninsula on the *Chief Wawatam*. For comparison's sake, in 1978, 2.5 million vehicles crossed the Mackinac Bridge.

How did the village of New Lothrop, in Shiawassee County, get its name?

    A.  From Paul Thorp, local baseball player
    B.  To distinguish it from Lathrup Village
    C.  They didn't like Old Lothrop.

**ANSWER: C**
They added the "New" to distinguish themselves from Lathrup Village, a city in Oakland County that is completely surrounded by the city of Southfield. It was founded in 1836 by local landowners Gideon Silverton, A. W. Gillette, Warren Williams, and Nathan Colby. It was originally called Lothrop for William Lothrop, who donated bells for the local Methodist church.

Paul Thorp (1907–1985) was a farmer in Wells Township, Michigan, a longtime superintendent of the old Berry School, and the author's grandfather.

How often does the Michigan Constitution say the legislature has to meet?

    A.  Once a year
    B.  Once a quarter

C. Once a month

**ANSWER: A**

The Michigan Constitution states that the legislature must meet at least once per year. No word on how long they must meet, just that they have to meet once every year.

---

These days, when we use the post office to mail a letter, it's called "snail mail." It really was snail mail in 1831, when mail began to arrive in Detroit every day.

How long did it take for mail to get from New York to Detroit in 1831?

A. 8 days
B. 14 days
C. 25 days

**ANSWER: B**

In 1831, when daily delivery to Detroit first began, it took a letter mailed in New York 14 days to get to Detroit.

---

The Detroit Lions are one of the oldest teams in the NFL. The franchise has been owned by William Clay Ford since 1964.

How much did Mr. Ford pay for the Lions in 1964?

A. $500,000
B. $1 million
C. $6 million

**ANSWER: C**

In January of 1964, William Clay Ford bought out his former partners in the Lions franchise for $6 million. Some estimates suggest that the franchise is worth in excess of $200 million today.

---

Do you like to fish? With all of its lakes, rivers, and streams, Michigan is a fisherman's paradise.

How large was the largest fish known to have been caught in Michigan waters?

How

A. 38 pounds
B. 97 pounds
C. 193 pounds

**ANSWER: C**
Believe it or not, a 193-pound, 87-inch-long lake sturgeon is the largest catch in Michigan history. It was caught by Joe Maka Jr. in 1974 on Mullett Lake in Cheboygan County.

How did the village of Kingston in Tuscola County get its name?

A. From Alanson King, the first settler
B. From King George
C. From King Kong

**ANSWER: A**
Kingston was named for Alanson King, the area's first settler. He arrived in 1857. In 1867, a post office was opened under the name Newbury, and the name was changed to Kingston in 1871.

How did Germfask, in the Upper Peninsula's Schoolcraft County, get its name?

A. Settlers were worried about germs.
B. It was named for the Germans from Fask, Germany.
C. It was named from the initials of the first settlers.

**ANSWER: C**
In 1881, Dr. W. W. French named the town using the first initials of the surnames of the area's first settlers.
John **G**rant
Mathew **E**dge
George **R**obinson
Thadeus **M**ead
Dr. W. W. **F**rench
Ezekial **A**ckley
Oscar **S**hepard
Hezekiah **K**naggs

How many counties does Michigan contain, in both the Upper and Lower peninsulas?

A. 64
B. 76
C. 83

**ANSWER: C**
Michigan has 83 counties: 15 in the Upper Peninsula and 68 in the Lower Peninsula. Michigan's first county was Wayne County, which at one time included most of Michigan and parts of Ohio, Illinois, and Wisconsin.

According to the Michigan Constitution, how long must you live in the state before you can register to vote?

A. 30 days
B. 6 months
C. 2 years

**ANSWER: B**
You can register to vote in Michigan after you have lived in the state for 6 months.

In Genesee County, in the city of Burton, there is a school district known as the Atherton School District. It is all that remains of a settlement called Atherton.
How did Atherton get its name?

A. It was named for ather trees found at the site.
B. From Shubael and Perus Atherton, first settlers
C. It was named for a city in England.

**ANSWER: B**
Atherton was named for brothers Shubael and Perus Atherton, who settled the area in 1834, along with Levi Gilkey. They named the community after the brothers and the creek after Levi Gilkey. By the way, there is no such thing as an ather tree.

How

Among consumers, the Michigan bottle return law is very popular. The law has helped eliminate a huge amount of trash along Michigan roads. Just before the law took effect in 1976, a survey was done to see how many items were tossed along the roads. From that, statisticians were able to estimate how much the law cut back on roadside trash.

How much did the returnable bottle law in Michigan reduce littering along Michigan roads?

A. 20%
B. 60%
C. 90%

ANSWER: C
The Michigan bottle bill is estimated to have cut 90% of trash along Michigan roads. Before the law took effect, more than 1.7 billion items were found along the roads; after the law took effect, that amount was reduced to 170 million items.

How many students were in the first class at Central Michigan University?

A. 15
B. 31
C. 212

ANSWER: B
Thirty-one students began their higher education in 1892 at what was then known as the Central Normal School and Business Institute. In 1895, the Michigan State Board of Education assumed control of the school, renaming it Central Michigan Normal School. Before WWII, the school's name changed to Central State Teachers College and then to Central Michigan College of Education. Finally, in 1959, it became Central Michigan University.

You might have heard of Fort Mackinac, Fort Wilkins, and Fort Wayne, all in Michigan and all still standing. Have you ever heard of Fort Hogan? It was built near Colon in 1832.

How long did Fort Hogan exist?

A. 3 days

256

B. 3 months

C. 3 years

**ANSWER: A**
Fort Hogan, named for the owner of the land where it was built, Daniel, was built in 1832 near Colon, Michigan, in St. Joseph County. It was abandoned after three days. The earthwork fort was built because of a perceived threat during the Black Hawk War by local militia.

One of the great adventure stories is the children's classic *The Wizard of Oz*. It was written by L. Frank Baum. It was made into one of the great movies of all time and generated other stories including *Wicked*, based on the Baum story and produced as a book and Broadway musical. There is a connection to Michigan.

How is *The Wizard of Oz* connected to Michigan?

A. Oz is set in Michigan.

B. *The Wizard of Oz* was written at Kelly Ruschman's childhood home in Davison, Michigan.

C. The Munchkins were from Michigan.

D. The second part was written while the author was vacationing near Holland, Michigan

**ANSWER: D**
L. Frank Baum spent the summer of 1907 in his cottage at Macatawa Park, near Holland. That is the summer he wrote the second installment of his story called "Ozma of Oz." It was the story about Munchkinland and the flying monkeys.

Kelly Ruschman is an advertising executive and wine connoisseur in Mequon, Wisconsin, and a close friend of the author. He grew up in Davison, but while he did see the movie, it was not written at his house.

Since 1828, Michigan has been the seat of the government, beginning with the Northwest Territory, the Michigan Territory, and the state of Michigan.

How many capitol buildings has Michigan had since 1828?

A. 3

B. 2

C. 1

**ANSWER: A**
Michigan has housed three capitol buildings since its inception: the first built in Detroit in 1828, the second built in Lansing in 1847, and the third, the current capital building, built in 1879.

How did the community of Mio get its name?

A. It was named for the Michigan Interstate Organization of Lumbermen.
B. From Mio T. Kolbe, founder
C. It is a mispronunciation.

**ANSWER: C**
Mio was founded in 1881 and was originally called "Mioe" in honor of the wife of town founder Henry Deyarmond. Her nieces and nephews had a hard time saying her name, "Aunt Maria"; they said "Aunt Mioe." The *e* was dropped in 1883, but no one seems to know why.

Sanilac County, in Michigan's Thumb, right on Lake Huron, was organized in 1848, about 10 years after the first European settler arrived.
How did Sanilac County get its name?

A. From Bob Sanilac, the first area settler
B. It's a Native American name for Lake Huron.
C. It was just made up.

**ANSWER: C**
Sanilac is just another one of the words that sounds like a Native American word that state geographer and geologist Henry Schoolcraft made up.

West Bloomfield, in Oakland County, is one of the most affluent areas in Michigan. It was founded in about 1833
How did West Bloomfield get its name?

A. From Westacres, a site of low-income housing
B. From the wild roses that bloomed there
C. From Zebediah Bloomfield, the first area settler

Believe it or not, West Bloomfield was founded as Westacres, a government housing project for low-income families starting during the Depression. In the early days, the area had apple orchards. In fact, the plentiful apple trees located on an island in one lake led to the naming of Orchard Lake and Apple Island.

The first Kmart store was opened in Garden City, Michigan, in 1962. That store is still open today.
How did Kmart get its name?

    A.  From Klean Market
    B.  From Krankies
    C.  From S. S. Kresge

**ANSWER: C**
Sebastian S. (S. S.) Kresge founded the S. S. Kresge dime store chain in Detroit in 1899. The company opened the first Kmart store on March 1, 1962, in Garden City, Michigan, to concentrate on discount products.

The city of New Buffalo, in Berrien County, was founded in 1834.
How did New Buffalo get its name?

    A.  From a buffalo heard
    B.  From Buffalo, New York
    C.  From Captain Whitaker Buffalo, founder and ship captain

**ANSWER: B**
In the autumn of 1834, Captain Wessel Whitaker ran his schooner the *Post Boy* aground near the site of the village of Grand Beach. While traveling to St. Joseph to report the ship's loss, Whitaker was struck by the beauty of the land and natural harbor. So he filed a claim to a large tract of land around the mouth of the Galien River and named it after his hometown of Buffalo, New York.

How

Michigan's most visible features are the Great Lakes.
How were the Great Lakes formed?

    A.  By the Great Flood
    B.  By an ancient ocean
    C.  By glaciers

**ANSWER: C**
It was glaciers of the last ice age that gouged out the lake bottoms as they expanded. As the glaciers melted, the water filled the great holes left by the gouging glaciers.

How does Michigan celebrate Labor Day in a way different from any other state?

A.  By walking a picket line
B.  By taking a five-mile hike
C.  By fishing for free

**ANSWER: B**
Labor Day is the only day that pedestrians are allowed to walk across the five-mile length of the Mackinac Bridge. The tradition started when Governor G. Mennen Williams led 15,000 people across the bridge in 1957, the year it opened. Thousands walk across every year, led by the governor of the state of Michigan.

Most people think of earthquakes as something that happens out west, in California, and overseas, but Michigan does have earthquakes. Most are too small to be felt without instruments. How often does an earthquake happen in Michigan?

A.  Every year
B.  Every five years
C.  Every 15–20 years

**ANSWER: C**
There is an earthquake we can feel about every 15–20 years. One you might have noticed was in September of 1980, when a quake broke windows and caused Tiger Stadium to sway. There was also a quake felt in Kalamazoo, on the west side of the state, in 2008.

One of the most interesting stories about a place name in Michigan is Whiskey Creek.
How did Whiskey Creek, in Oceana County, get its name?

A.  From a moonshine still
B.  From its whiskey-drinking founder

C. From magic reproducing barrels

**ANSWER: C**
George Stewart lived in a house/store over the creek in the 1840s. He was said to have "laid in" one barrel of whiskey in the fall. Over the winter, he sold three barrels and somehow had two more in the spring. Some locals called it the miracle of the reproducing barrels and thought it might have something to do with the creek under Stewart's house, so it became Whiskey Creek.

How did the village of Dundee, in Monroe County, get its name?

A. It was named for the homeland of the postmaster's family.
B. It was named for Don and Dee Lada, early settlers.
C. It was a Native American word for "river crossing."

**ANSWER: A**
Dundee was first settled in 1823 on the River Raisin. It was a fine site for a mill. In the early 1830s, a Mr. S. Van Ness laid out the village and called it Van Ness Mills. In 1836, a post office was established in the village proper under Postmaster Alonzo Curtis, who had named the township Dundee after the city in Scotland where his family came from. He gave the village the same name. The name in Scottish Gaelic probably means "fort" (**dun**) and perhaps "fire" (**deagh**).

Donald and Dee Lada are longtime friends of the author. Donald, a funeral director, and his wife, Dee, are well known for their community efforts, especially their dedication to our military veterans and their devotion to children.

How did Midland, Michigan, get its name?

A. It's in the middle of the state.
B. From Dow Midland, the first settler
C. From Midland, Texas

**ANSWER: A**
The city of Midland was named for the county it is in, and the county was named Midland because it is in the middle of the state.

How did Bay County's University Center, Michigan, get its name?

A. The first settler was a University of Michigan graduate.
B. The area was designated for colleges.

C. It was the geographical center of all Michigan colleges and universities.

**ANSWER: B**
University Center, Michigan, got a post office in July of 1961. It was named University Center by the U.S. Post Office because it had been set aside to build a place of higher learning. Delta College was opened in September of 1961, and Saginaw Valley State University was opened in September of 1964.

The legend of the first Holland marching band is a fascinating story.
According to legend, how did Holland get its first marching band?

A. It was created for the mayor's wedding.
B. Its uniforms and instruments were donated.
C. It was work for unemployed residents.

**ANSWER: B**
Holland was practically burned to the ground in the Great Fires of 1871. That is the same fire that burned Chicago and a good portion of Michigan and Wisconsin. After that, people from all over the country donated items to the city, such as clothes, farm equipment, tools, food, and band equipment, including uniforms and instruments. The local citizens are said to have put the uniforms and instruments to good use and learned to play them. The only reported performance by the band was at the Muskegon Band Festival, where the band members played the only song they knew, "Marching through Georgia," all day.

Titus Bronson is credited with being the founder of Kalamazoo, Michigan. He was also known as Potato Bronson.
How did Titus "Potato" Bronson get his nickname?

A. He invented Mr. Potato Head.
B. He grew potatoes.
C. He looked like a potato.

**ANSWER: B**
In the early 1800s, Bronson discovered a new variety of potatoes near Akron, Ohio, and began going from town to town growing potatoes. By 1823, he grew

the first potatoes known to have been grown in Ann Arbor. In 1829, he founded Bronson, which later became Kalamazoo.

In the late 1860s, a Flint woman named Sarah Edmonds became famous all over the country.
How did she gain her fame?

A. She was the first woman in the legislature.
B. She was the only woman Civil War veteran.
C. She was the first woman doctor.

**ANSWER: B**
Sarah Edmonds was the only woman to be confirmed a Civil War veteran. She disguised herself as a man named Franklin Thompson and served in combat. She was the only woman to be welcomed into the G. A. R. and to get a pension from the government.

The youngest man to serve as Michigan governor was Stevens T. Mason, the state's first governor. He was known as the "boy governor."
How old was Governor Mason when he took office?

A. 19
B. 23
C. 28

**ANSWER: A**
Governor Mason took office after his father's death in 1831 when he was just 19 years old. He was born in Virginia and came to Michigan in 1830 when President Andrew Jackson appointed his father, John, secretary of the Michigan Territory. He became governor in his own right five years later and served until 1840. Stevens T. Mason died of pneumonia in New York in 1843 at the age of 31.

There are Bois Blanc Islands all over the Great Lakes, and they are all known as Boblo Island because of the way the English corrupted the word. One "Boblo" is just southeast of Mackinac Island in Lake Huron. The island covers about 34 square miles and has six lakes.
How did Bois Blanc Island get its name?

How

A. It was named for Bob Bois, an early explorer.

B. It is a French word.

C. It is a Native American word for "white canoe."

**ANSWER: B**

"Bois Blanc" is French for "white wood." Most likely, it refers to birch or basswood trees common on Great Lakes islands. Native Americans used strips of these trees to make canoes and snowshoes. The Native Americans called the islands Wigobiminiss, which means the bark used to tie things; the French traders called those strips "bois blancs."

Bob Bois is a friend of the author and an active volunteer for the Boy Scouts as a council vice president. He works in the insurance industry with his family's Bois Insurance Agency, founded in 1919 in Flushing, Michigan.

If you have interesting stories, compelling trivia questions, or any other handy nuggets of Great Lakes information you'd like to share, please send it to *Greatlakestriviatest.com* or *michealjthorp.com* and we may incorporate it into the next book!